Annals of Mathematics Studies
Number 47

ANNALS OF MATHEMATICS STUDIES

Edited by Robert C. Gunning, John C. Moore, and Marston Morse

1. Algebraic Theory of Numbers, *by* HERMANN WEYL
3. Consistency of the Continuum Hypothesis, *by* KURT GÖDEL
11. Introduction to Nonlinear Mechanics, *by* N. KRYLOFF *and* N. BOGOLIUBOFF
16. Transcendental Numbers, *by* CARL LUDWIG SIEGEL
19. Fourier Transforms, *by* S. BOCHNER *and* K. CHANDRASEKHARAN
20. Contributions to the Theory of Nonlinear Oscillations, Vol. I, *edited by* S. LEFSCHETZ
21. Functional Operators, Vol. I, *by* JOHN VON NEUMANN
24. Contributions to the Theory of Games, Vol. I, *edited by* H. W. KUHN *and* A. W. TUCKER
25. Contributions to Fourier Analysis, *edited by* A. ZYGMUND, W. TRANSUE, M. MORSE, A. P. CALDERON, *and* S. BOCHNER
28. Contributions to the Theory of Games, Vol. II, *edited by* H. W. KUHN *and* A. W. TUCKER
29. Contributions to the Theory of Nonlinear Oscillations, Vol. II, *edited by* S. LEFSCHETZ
30. Contributions to the Theory of Riemann Surfaces, *edited by* L. AHLFORS *et al.*
33. Contributions to the Theory of Partial Differential Equations, *edited by* L. BERS, S. BOCHNER, *and* F. JOHN
34. Automata Studies, *edited by* C. E. SHANNON *and* J. MCCARTHY
36. Contributions to the Theory of Nonlinear Oscillations, Vol. III, *edited by* S. LEFSCHETZ
38. Linear Inequalities and Related Systems, *edited by* H. W. KUHN *and* A. W. TUCKER
39. Contributions to the Theory of Games, Vol. III, *edited by* M. DRESHER, A. W. TUCKER *and* P. WOLFE
40. Contributions to the Theory of Games, Vol. IV, *edited by* R. DUNCAN LUCE *and* A. W. TUCKER
41. Contributions to the Theory of Nonlinear Oscillations, Vol. IV, *edited by* S. LEFSCHETZ
42. Lectures on Fourier Integrals, *by* S. BOCHNER. In preparation
43. Ramification Theoretic Methods in Algebraic Geometry, *by* S. ABHYANKAR
44. Stationary Processes and Prediction Theory, *by* H. FURSTENBERG
45. Contributions to the Theory of Nonlinear Oscillations, Vol. V, CESARI, LASALLE, *and* LEFSCHETZ
46. Seminar on Transformation Groups, *by* A. BOREL *et al.*
47. Theory of Formal Systems, *by* R. SMULLYAN
48. Lectures on Modular Forms, *by* R. C. GUNNING
49. Composition Methods in Homotopy Groups of Spheres, *by* H. TODA
50. Cohomology Operations, *lectures by* N. E. STEENROD, *written and revised by* D. B. A. EPSTEIN
51. Morse Theory, *by* J. W. MILNOR
52. Advances in Game Theory, *edited by* M. DRESHER, L. SHAPLEY, *and* A. W. TUCKER
53. Flows on Homogeneous Spaces, *by* L. AUSLANDER, L. GREEN, F. HAHN, *et al.*
54. Elementary Differential Topology, *by* J. R. MUNKRES
55. Degrees of Recursive Unsolvability, *by* G. E. SACKS. In preparation

THEORY OF FORMAL SYSTEMS

BY

Raymond M. Smullyan

REVISED EDITION

PRINCETON, NEW JERSEY
PRINCETON UNIVERSITY PRESS
1961

L. C. Card 60-14063

This research was mainly supported jointly by the Department of the Army, the Department of the Navy, and the Department of the Air Force under Air Force Contract No. AF 19(604)-5200. It was also supported in part by a National Science Foundation grant-in-aid in Knot Theory and Metamathematics, Mathematics Department, Princeton University.

Printed in the United States of America

To the memory of my father

PREFACE

This study combines an introduction to recursive function theory (and its applications to metamathematics) with a presentation of new results in the field. The author has particularly borne in mind the needs of the generally mature mathematician with no background in mathematical logic. Our treatment (particularly in Chapters I and II) has been mainly influenced by the elegant methods of Post.

Chapter I commences with a new characterization of "formal mathmatical systems" and "recursively enumerable sets and relations". We introduce the notion of an "elementary formal system" which serves as the basic formalism for the entire study. A very short and simple proof is given of Church's theorem — that there exists no uniform "algorithm" for deciding which sentences are provable in which mathematical systems. The proof is in the spirit of Post, but the normal form theorem for canonical systems is avoided. The study of elementary formal systems is continued in Chapter II, which consists mainly of results of a preliminary nature for the remaining chapters.

In Chapter III we approach the Gödel and Rosser incompleteness theorems and related results on undecidability, from a highly abstract point of view. The usual machinery of mathematical logic (the propositional and first order functional calculi) is not employed. The applications to mathematical logic proper are treated separately in the supplement. The results on undecidability are all deduced from a tiny fragment of recursive function theory developed in #A of Chapter II. Chapter III also extends some well known metamathematical results; these are further extended in Chapter V.

Chapter IV contains a connected presentation of recursive function theory from a viewpoint which combines the theory of elementary formal systems with an extension of Quine's techniques of concatenation theory. [The reader whose main interest is in recursive functions can read this chapter directly following Chapter II.] Gödel's program of arithmetizing syntax is accomplished in a new manner; no appeal is made to primitive recursive function theory, prime factorization, theory of congruences or the Chinese remainder theorem. A by-product of this approach (which was undertaken primarily out of considerations of elegance) is the improved normal form theorems are obtained.

The concluding chapter contains the results of the author's recent research on the theory of universal sets and double universal pairs. A particularly interesting application, jointly due to Hilary Putnam and the author, is given in the concluding section of the supplement.

This study is a revision of the author's doctoral dissertation [31]. The author wishes to express his thanks to Alonzo Church, John Myhill and Hilary Putnam for their kind encouragement and help. For help in proof reading, the author is indebted to Marshal Freimer, Robert Richie, Alan Tritter, Robert Windor, and particularly to James Guard. For spotting misprints and errors in the first edition, the author is indebted to Robert Cowen, John Graves, R. N. Herstein, Joel Pitt, Jerry Siegel, Professor W. Stegmüller, and to a student of Professor Fitch. Particular thanks are due to Thomas G. McLaughlin for his critical remarks concerning the original version of Chapter V.

Raymond M. Smullyan

New York, N. Y.
November, 1962

TABLE OF CONTENTS

CONTENTS

CHAPTER I: FORMAL MATHEMATICAL SYSTEMS

In this chapter, we are interested in first giving a precise definition of a "formal" or "finitary" mathematical system, and then in establishing an important theorem, based on the works of Church and Post, concerning an interesting limitation of our possible knowledge of such systems. This theorem, which we can only state quite crudely at this stage, is essentially to the effect that there exists no decision procedure for formalized mathematics. Stated otherwise, there exists no "mechanical" method which will decide which sentences are provable in which mathematical systems. We shall subsequently use this theorem to prove and extend some of Gödel's famous incompleteness theorems.

The notions of "formal", as applied to mathematical systems, and "mechanical" as applied to operations (or procedures) remain to be defined; this shall be done in this chapter. Intuitively we think of a mechanical operation as one which is capable of being performed by a "computing machine", but again we must define just what a computing machine is. The notions of formal system and mechanical operation are intimately connected; either can be defined in terms of the other. If we should first define a mechanical operation directly (e.g., in terms of Turing machines), we would then define a "formal" system as one whose set of theorems could be generated by such a machine (that is to say, the machine grinds out all the theorems, one after another, but never grinds out a non-theorem). Alternatively (following the lines of Post), we can first define a formal system directly and define an operation to be "mechanical" or "recursive" if it is computable in some formal systems. This is the approach we shall take. Our plan is to define first a certain type of system termed an "elementary formal system" which will serve as a basis for our study of metamethematics (theory of mathematical systems). The general notion of a "formal system" will then be defined in terms of these elementary systems.[1]

---

[1] Elementary Formal Systems can be looked at as variants of the canonical languages of Post [16]. The advantage of working in Post-like systems is that we can thereby develop considerable portions of the theory of formal expressions in a direct manner, rather than by the device of "Gödel numbering". The reason for our choice of elementary formal systems, in lieu of

#A. ELEMENTARY FORMAL SYSTEMS

§0. Motivation. The purpose of elementary formal systems is to explicate the notion of "definability by recursion". We refer to the following type of definition, which is frequent in the mathematical literature: Instead of defining a set (or relation) W outright, W is sometimes defined by first giving a set of axioms for membership in W, then certain axioms of the form "if such and such and so and so are in W, then such and such a combination of them is also in W". Then the final axiom (which might be called the "recursion clause") "furthermore, nothing is in W unless its being so follows from the preceding axioms". Now, it is this last clause which must be made precise. One might ask "follows from in what logic?". Elementary formal systems provide one such type of logic.

We consider a simple example: Let K be the alphabet consisting of the two signs a and b. Suppose we wish to define the set S of all strings of the two signs a and b which alternate with a and b — i.e., which contain no two consecutive occurrences of a or of b. We can implicitly define this set S by stipulating the following axioms for membership in S:

AXIOM 1. a is an element of S

AXIOM 2. b is an element of S

AXIOM 3. ab is an element of S

AXIOM 4. ba is an element of S

AXIOM 5. If xa is an element of S (where x is any string) then xab is an element of S.

AXIOM 6. If xb is an element of S then xba is an element of S.

*AXIOM 7. No element is in S unless its being so follows from Axioms 1-6.

We now convert the above informal axiom system into a precise formal system. We firstly abbreviate any such phrase as "x is an element of S" by "x ϵ S" or better still "Sx" (the latter is to be read "S contains x"). We also abbreviate any such phrase as "if (——) then (----)"

1 (continued)

Post's canonical systems, is that their structure is more simply described, and their techniques are more easily applied. The general notion of "production" used in Post systems is replaced by the simpler logistic rules of substitution and detachment (modus ponens), which are more easily formalized. It is of interest that these two rules, so familiar in symbolic logic, do indeed constitute a basis for the construction of all formal systems (as they are to be defined).

by the usual symbolic abbreviation "(——) ——> (----)". We now rewrite our axioms in symbolic form thus:

1) Sa
2) Sb
3) Sab
4) Sba
5) Sxa ——> Sxab
6) Sxb ——> Sxba

Now, instead of Axiom 7, we give the following precise definition of "follows from": A string X is said to follow from the Axioms (1) - (6) if and only if X can be obtained from these six axioms by a finite number of applications of the following two rules:

R_1. To substitute any string in the signs a and b for the variable x.

R_2. From two strings X_1 and X_1 ——> X_2, the string X_2 may be derived.

We can now define our desired set S as the set of all strings X (in a and b) such that the symbol "S" followed by X is derivable from (1) - (6) by using R_1 and R_2. In this system we say that the symbol "S" represents the set of all alternating strings.

The above is a simple example of an elementary formal system. The symbols a and b are called the initial signs; "x" is called a variable (for which we substitute strings in the initial signs). The symbol "——>" is called the implication sign, and finally the letter "S" is an example of a predicate (predicates are used to represent sets and relations).

With this example in mind, we now give a precise definition of elementary formal systems.

§1. DEFINITION OF AN ELEMENTARY FORMAL SYSTEM

Preliminary Notions. By an alphabet K we mean an ordered finite set of elements called symbols, signs, or letters of K. Any finite linear sequence (ordered n-tuple) of symbols of K is called a word or an expression or a string in K. We let $\underline{K}$ be the set of all words in K. For any n symbols $x_1, x_2, \ldots, x_n$ of K we let $x_1x_2\ldots x_n$ be that word in K whose i-th symbol is $x_i [i \leq n]$. We call n the length of this word. If Y is also a word $y_1y_2\ldots y_m$ in K, we define XY to be the word $x_1x_2\ldots x_ny_1y_2\ldots y_m$ — i.e., that word of length n + m whose i-th symbol is x_i, for $i \leq n$, and whose j-th symbol is y_{j-n}, for $j > n$. We call XY the product or concatenation of X and Y. The operation of concatenation is clearly associative, but non-commutative (unless K contains only one symbol). If K and L are alphabets and if every symbol of K is also a symbol of L, then we call K a sub-alphabet of L (written: $K \subseteq L$), and also L an extension of K.

Definition of an Elementary Formal System. By an elementary formal system (E) over an alphabet K, we mean a collection of the following items:

(1) The alphabet K.
(2) Another alphabet of symbols called variables.
(3) Another alphabet of symbols called predicates, each of which is assigned a unique positive integer called its degree.
(4) Two more symbols called the implication sign and the punctuation sign.
(5) A finite sequence $A_1, \ldots, A_z$ of strings which are well formed formulas, according to the definition given below; these strings are called the axioms of the system (E).

The alphabets (1) - (4) are to be mutually disjoint. The elements of K will usually be denoted by "a" or "b", with or without subscripts. The variable will be denoted by "x", "y", "z", "w", "v", with or without subscripts. The predicates will usually be denoted by "P" with or without subscripts. The implication sign (also called the "arrow") will usually be denoted by "$\longrightarrow$". The punctuation sign (also called the "comma") will usually be denoted by a comma.

Let $a_1, a_2, \ldots, a_n$ be the symbols of K. By a term t of (E) we mean any string composed of the a_i and variables (or either one alone) e.g., $a_1xya_2ya_1$ is a term. By an atomic (well formed) formula of (E) we mean an expression of the form $Pt_1, \ldots, t_m$, where P is a predicate of degree m and $t_1, \ldots, t_m$ are terms. By a well formed formula (sometimes written "w.f.f." or sometimes just "formula") F of (E) we mean either an atomic (well formed) formula F_1 or an expression of the form $F_1 \longrightarrow F_2 \longrightarrow \cdots \longrightarrow F_n$, where each F_i is atomic. The atomic formulas $F_1, \ldots, F_n$ are called the atomic components of the compound formula $F_1 \longrightarrow F_2 \longrightarrow \cdots \longrightarrow F_n$. Also, any atomic formula F_1 is called an atomic component of itself. In a compound formula $F_1 \longrightarrow F_2 \longrightarrow \cdots \longrightarrow F_n$, the arrow is to be interpreted as implication with association to the right; e.g., "$F_1 \longrightarrow F_2 \longrightarrow F_3$" is to be read "$F_1$ implies that F_2 implies F_3" or "F_1 implies (F_2 implies F_3)". We note that this can also be read "If F_1 and F_2 are both true, so is F_3". More generally, $F_1 \longrightarrow F_2 \longrightarrow \cdots \longrightarrow F_n$ can be read "F_n is implied by the conjunction of the premisses $F_1, F_2, \ldots, F_{n-1}$". We, in fact, refer to $F_1, \ldots, F_{n-1}$ as the premisses and F_n as the conclusion. We note in passing, that for two arbitrary w.f.f.s X_1 and X_2, it is a mistake to read $X_1 \longrightarrow X_2$ as "X_1 implies X_2"; this can only be done providing X_1 is atomic. because of the def of wff and the association rule

By an <u>instance</u> of a w.f.f. X is meant any string obtained from X by substituting strings in K for all variables. A w.f.f. with no variables is called a <u>sentence</u>.

By a <u>theorem</u> or <u>provable</u> string of (E) is meant any string which is either an axiom of (E), or is derivable from the axioms of (E) by a finite number of applications of the following two rules - called "rules of inference"

Rule I. Substitution of words in K for variables.

Rule II. (Rule of Detachment or Modus Ponens). Inferring formula X_2 from X_1 and $X_1 \longrightarrow X_2$, providing X_1 is atomic.

The reason for the proviso in Rule II - that X_1 be atomic - is that otherwise the rule of modus ponens would not be faithful to the intended interpretation of the implication sign (we recall that we can interpret "$X_1 \longrightarrow X_2$" as "X_1 implies X_2", only in the case that X_1 is atomic).

REMARKS. Let (E) be an E.F.S. (elementary formal system) over an alphabet K. Let K' be the alphabet consisting of the symbols of K, together with the variables, predicates, implication sign and punctuation sign of (E). It may sometimes happen that we wish to consider simultaneously an E.F.S. (E)' over the alphabet K'; if this happens, then the variables of (E) are not variables of (E)', but are rather some of the initial symbols of (E)' (and we must then be careful to use different names for the two classes of variables -- cf. Appendix to this chapter). Similar remarks apply to the predicates, implication sign and punctuation sign. Thus these grammatical categories are only relative to a given E.F.S.

§2. ALTERNATIVE FORMULATION OF ELEMENTARY FORMAL SYSTEMS

Any <u>sentence</u> derivable from $A_1, \ldots, A_z$ by substitution and modus ponens, can as well be derived from the instances of $A_1, \ldots, A_z$ by modus ponens alone. That is, in any derivation involving both substitution and detachment, we could first make all necessary substitutions in the A_i and then perform the detachments (this fact can be established rigorously by a simple induction argument). Thus an alternative manner (using a device of von Neumann) of regarding elementary formal systems is as follows:

We again consider the sequence of w.f.f.s $A_1, \ldots, A_z$, but now each A_i instead of being called an axiom of the system is called an axiom schema; the axioms are now defined to be the instances of the axiom schemata. Thus an elementary formal system (looked at in the second sense) has an infinite number of axioms, but a finite number of axiom schemata. A theorem would then be defined as any sentence derivable from the axioms (i.e., instances of the axiom schemata) by successive application of modus ponens. As remarked before, the sentences provable in an E.F.S. are the same regardless of which of the two senses we use.

§3. REPRESENTABILITY

Let P be predicate of degree 1 in an elementary formal system (E) over K, and let W be a set of words in K. We say that P represents W in (E) iff[2] for every word X in K, the following condition holds:

$$X \in W \Longleftrightarrow PX \text{ is provable in } (E) .$$

Analogously, if P is a predicate of (E) of degree n, then we say that P represents the set of all n-tuples $(X_1, \ldots, X_n)$ such that $PX_1, \ldots, X_n$ is provable in (E).

We henceforth use the term "attribute" as a collective term for sets and relations; more precisely for any set S, an attribute in S is either a subset of S or a set of n-tuples of elements of S.[3]

An attribute W of words in K is called formally representable over K (abbreviated "f.r. over K") iff W is representable in some elementary formal system over K. W is called solvable over K iff both W and its complement $\tilde{W}$ are f.r. over K. [For W a relation of degree n, $\tilde{W}$ is understood to be the complement of W relative to the set of all n-tuples of words in K.]

The following interesting question arises: If W is an attribute in K and L is an extension of K and if W is representable in some E.F.S. over L, is W necessarily representable in some E.F.S. over K? We shall subsequently answer this question affirmatively. (If K contains

---

[2] We use "iff " to abbreviate "if and only if". (This notation is due to Halmos.) Other abbreviations we shall use are "$\Longleftrightarrow$" and "$\longleftrightarrow$".

[3] Our use of the term "attribute" is non-standard; the word usually means a property or relation in the intensional sense. However no ambiguity can possibly arise within this study, since the latter notion will never be used.

at least 2 symbols, the solution is quite simple; if K contains only one symbol, the solution is more elaborate.)

EXAMPLES

a) Let K be the alphabet consisting of the single sign "1". We identify a string of "1"s of length n with the positive integer n. Suppose we wish to construct an E.F.S. over "1" in which we represent the set of even numbers.[4] We take a predicate which we will call "E" to represent this set, and the variable "x". We take the following axioms:

E11

Ex ⟶ Ex11

In this system, we can prove a string EX (X is a string of "1"s) if and only if X is even, hence E represents the set of even numbers.

REMARKS. To prove, for the above system, that the letter "E" does in fact represent the set of even numbers, we must prove: (i) for any even number X, EX is provable in the system; (ii) if EX is provable in the system, then X is even.

We can prove (i) by mathematical induction: Let $e_1, e_2, \ldots, e_n, \ldots$ be the sequence of all even numbers. For n = 1, Ee_1 - viz. E11 - is provable in the system. Suppose for the i-th even number e_i, that Ee_i is provable in the system. Also $Ee_i \longrightarrow Ee_i11$ is provable (this is a substitution instance of the second axiom). Hence, since Ee_i and $Ee_i \longrightarrow Ee_i11$ are provable, then Ee_i11 is provable; this completes the induction.

To prove (ii), it is perhaps easiest to give an <u>interpretation</u> to the system. Define an atomic expression of the form EX (where X is a string of "1"s) to be <u>true</u> iff X is even; for any expression of the form $EX_1 \longrightarrow EX_2$, define it to be true iff EX_1 is true implies EX_2 is true. It is now trivial to verify that both axioms of the system are true (for all numbers x) and that the rule of detachment preserves truth - thus all theorems of the system are true. Hence for any string X (of "1"s), if EX is provable then EX is true - i.e., X is even. This proves (ii).

We have gone to considerable length to spell out all the mathematical reasoning involved in the above proof for this very simple elementary formal system. We have done this in order to provide the reader with a model of how such proofs can be carried out for all the elementary

---

[4] The word "number" in this study always means "positive integer", unless the contrary is specified.

formal systems which will be constructed in this and the next chapter. We shall henceforth present only the elementary formal systems and specify which predicates represent which attributes; the proof that these predicates do indeed represent these attributes will always be left to the reader (they are trivial and straight-forward in all cases).

b) Let K be the 3-sign alphabet "a", "b", "c". Let W be the set of all strings in K which involve only the two signs "a" and "b". We wish to show that W is f.r. [formally representable] over K. We take the following elementary formal system (E):

Wa

Wb

Wx ⟶ Wy ⟶ Wxy

Then "W" represents W in (E).

REMARK. We note that in the last example, we have used, for the predicate to represent W, the symbol "W" itself. There is no reason why we should not allow the metalinguistic name of a set (or relation) to be the very same as the letter used to represent it in an elementary formal system. We shall do this frequently.

c) More generally let K be an alphabet $(a_1, \ldots, a_m, \ldots, a_n)$ and J the sub-alphabet $(a_1, \ldots, a_m)$. We wish to show that the set $\underline{J}$ of all words in J is f.r. over K. Well, this set is represented by P in the elementary formal systems:

Pa_1

⋮

Pa_m

Px ⟶ Py ⟶ Pxy

d) Suppose we wish to show that the above set $\underline{J}$ is <u>solvable</u> over K. It remains to show that $\underline{K} - \underline{J}$ is f.r. over K. Now, $\underline{K} - \underline{J}$ consists of all words in K in which at least one symbol of K - J occurs at least once. Thus $\underline{K} - \underline{J}$ is represented by P in that E.F.S. over K whose axioms are:

Pa_{m+1}

⋮

Pa_n

Px ⟶ Pxy

Px ⟶ Pyx

FUNCTIONS. A function $f(x_1, \ldots, x_n)$ from n-tuples of words in K to words in K is called formally representable over K iff the relation

$f(x_1, \ldots, x_n) = y$ is formally representable over K, and solvable over K iff the relation is solvable over K.

§4. MATHEMATICAL SYSTEMS

By a mathematical system (M) is usually meant a collection of at least the following items:

(1) An alphabet K

(2) A set A of words in K called axioms

(3) A finite set $R_1, \ldots, R_m$ of relations in K called rules of inference.

By a proof in M is meant any sequence $(X_1, X_2, \ldots, X_n)$ of words in K such that for each $i \leq n$ either X_i is an axiom or else there exists numbers $i_1, \ldots, i_r$ all less than i such that $X_{i_1}, \ldots, X_{i_r}, X_i)$ stands in one of the relations $R_1, \ldots, R_m$. A proof $(X_1, \ldots, X_n)$ is also called a proof of the last term X_n. A word X is called provable in (M) or a theorem of (M) iff there exists a proof of it in (M). The set of all theorems of (M) shall be denoted by "T".

We now define (M) to be a formal mathematical system iff the set T of theorems of (M) is formally representable over K.[5] If T is solvable over K then (M) is called solvable or decidable or to admit of a decision procedure. Church's important theorem (which we are aiming at) is that there exist formal systems for which there is no decision procedure.

Informal discussion. A complete knowledge of elementary formal systems would mean a complete knowledge of all formal systems, for if (M) is a formal system which is represented by P in some elementary formal system (E) (i.e., the set of theorems of (M) is so represented) then the question as to whether or not a string X is a theorem of (M) is equivalent to the question of whether or not PX is a theorem of (E). The answers must be the same, by definition of representability. Thus any question about provability in formal systems is reducible to a question about elementary formal systems.

We can now think of a "computing machine" as any machine which

---

[5] This definition does in fact cover all mathematical systems so far constructed in the literature which would be called "formal" or "finitory" on intuitive grounds. Such systems as Principia Mathematica, Zermelo Set Theory, the lower functional calculus, formal number theory, combinatory logics, etc.; all these are representable in elementary formal systems. Post defines a formal system as one whose set of theorems is representable in a canonical system. Since this latter is equivalent to representability in an E.F.S., our definition of "formal system" is equivalent to Post's.

generates some formally representable set. If W is a solvable set, then we can construct two computing machines M and M' which respectively generate $\tilde{W}$ and W'. To determine whether a given string X is or is not in W, we set both machines going simultaneously and simply wait to see which machine comes up with X; sooner or later one of them will. If, on the other hand, W is formally representable but not solvable, then the best that can be done is to construct one machine M which generates W. If X is in W, then sooner or later we will know it, since M will come up with it. If however X is not in W, then we can wait forever, and at no time can we be sure that X may not turn up in the future.

#B. RECURSIVE ENUMERABILITY

§5. RECURSIVELY ENUMERABLE ATTRIBUTES OF POSITIVE INTEGERS

Let us now consider the two-sign alphabet whose symbols are "1" and "2"; call this alphabet "D". Any elementary formal system over D will be called an elementary dyadic arithmetic. A string $d_n d_{n-1} \ldots d_1 d_o$, where each d_i is either "1" or "2", is called a dyadic numeral and represents the number $d_o + 2d_1 + 4d_2 + \ldots + 2^n d_n$. This representation of numbers, which we call dyadic is, like the usual binary representation using "0" and "1", unique; moreover it has, for our purposes, certain technical advantages. In this chapter we shall identify the dyadic numerals with the numbers which they represent. We note that if we order the dyadic numerals lexicographically - i.e., according to length and alphabetically within each group of the same length - then the position which any numeral has, in this sequence, is the same as the number which it designates.

We now define a recursively enumerable attribute of positive integers as one which is representable in some elementary dyadic arithmetic. A recursively enumerable attribute whose complement is also recursively enumerable is called recursive.

REMARKS. In our definition of recursive enumerability, our choice of 2 as a base was of course arbitrary, but will prove to be technically extremely convenient. In the next chapter we will show that whatever base n we chose, the definition of "recursively enumerable" would be equivalent.

We have defined recursive enumerability only for attributes of positive integers. But this can be easily extended to a definition of r.e. for attributes of non-negative integers, as follows: For any attribute $W(x_1, \ldots, x_n)$ of non-negative integers, define W^+ by the condition: $W^+(x_1+1, \ldots, x_n+1) \iff W(x_1, \ldots, x_n)$. Then we can define W to be a r.e. attribute of non-negative integers iff W^+ is a r.e. attribute of positive integers. However, we shall be concerned with r.e. attributes of positive integers only.

§6. GÖDEL NUMBERING

As an informal introduction to the motivation for Gödel numbering, suppose we have a theory which talks about positive integers. We are interested in "keeping track" of the sentences of the theory within the theory itself; this cannot be done directly since the theory talks about numbers and not about sentences. We can, however, achieve the same result indirectly by assigning a number to each sentence (the so-called "Gödel number" of the sentence) and then translating any statement about the sentences to the corresponding statement about their Gödel numbers.

Consider an alphabet K. By a Gödel numbering of K we shall simply mean any 1 - 1 function g from K into (not necessarily onto) the set N of positive integers. Thus g is a 1 - 1 mapping which assigns to each word X in K a unique positive integer g(X). We shall frequently write X_o for g(X), and for any attribute W in K, W_o shall be the corresponding attribute of Gödel numbers -- i.e., $W_o = g(W) =$ set of n-tuples $(g(X_1), \ldots, g(X_n))$ such that $(X_1, \ldots, X_n) \in W$.

There are two types of Gödel correspondences which we shall frequently employ in this study. (Still a third type will be employed in Chapter IV.) Let K be an ordered alphabet $(a_1, a_2, \ldots, a_n)$. We wish to assign Gödel numbers to all the strings in K. The first type of Gödel numbering, which we shall call the lexicographical Gödel numbering, consists simply of ordering all the strings in K in lexicographical sequence, and then assigning to each string, its position in that sequence. We note that all positive integers are used up in this correspondence (i.e., g is onto N)

The second type of Gödel correspondence, which we shall call the dyadic Gödel correspondence, shall consist in assigning to each string X the (dyadic) numeral (number) which results from X by replacing each occurrence of a_1 by 12, a_2 by 122, ..., a_n by $1\underbrace{22\ldots2}_{n}$ - e.g., the dyadic Gödel number of $a_3a_4a_1a_2$ is 12221222212122. To simplify our notation, let us henceforth abbreviate the numerals 12, 122, 1222, ..., etc., respectively, by "g_1", "g_2", "g_3", ..., etc. . Thus the dyadic Gödel number of $a_3a_4a_1a_2$ is $g_3g_4g_1g_2$.

We note that the dyadic Gödel correspondence has the nice technical advantage of being an isomorphism with respect to concatenation -- i.e., if x is the dyadic Gödel number of X and y of Y, then xy (i.e., x followed by y) is the Gödel number of XY. Stated otherwise, $(XY)_o = X_oY_o$.

We shall call a Gödel numbering admissible iff it satisfies the condition that for every attribute W in K, W is f.r. over K iff W_o is r.e. and W is solvable over K iff W_o is recursive. In Chapter II we shall show that both the lexicographical and the dyadic Gödel numberings are admissible.

The dyadic correspondence is the only one which we shall use in this chapter. We let g be the function which assigns to each string X its (dyadic) Gödel number X_o. If the symbols "1" and "2" are themselves in K, then every numeral n itself has a Gödel number n_o; we let g_o be the function which assigns to each n the number n_o. It will be convenient to order K so that "1" and "2" are respectively the first 2 symbols. Then $g_o(1) = 12$ and $g_o(2) = 122$, and for any number xy, $g_o(xy)$ is $g_o(x)$ followed by $g_o(y)$ (here xy means x followed by y, not x times y). We note that the relation $g(x) = y$ is f.r. over K, since it is represented by "P" in that E.F.S. over K whose axioms are:

$$\begin{array}{l} Pl, 12 \\ P2, 122 \\ Pa_3, 1222 \\ \vdots \\ Pa_n, 1\underbrace{22\ldots2}_{n} \\ Px, y \longrightarrow Pz, w \longrightarrow Pxz, yw . \end{array}$$

Also the relation $g_o(x) = y$ is r.e. (f.r. over D), since it is represented by P in that recursive dyadic arithmetic (E.F.S. over D) whose axioms are:

$$\begin{array}{l} P1, 12 \\ P2, 122 \\ Pxy \longrightarrow Pz, w \longrightarrow Pxz, yw \end{array}$$

§7. THE UNIVERSAL SYSTEM U

We now wish to construct a so-called "Universal System" in which we can, so to speak, express all propositions of the form that such and such a number is in such and such a recursively enumerable set.

Preparatory to the construction of U, we need a device for "transcribing" all elementary dyadic arithmetics into one single finite alphabet. Let us define a transcribed elementary dyadic arithmetic (henceforth abbreviated "T.A.") to be a system like an elementary dyadic arithmetic except that instead of taking our variables and predicates to be individual symbols, we take 3 signs v, ', p and define a variable to be any of the words v', v", v''', etc. and a <u>predicate</u> to be a string of p's followed by a string of accents; the number of p's is to indicate the <u>degree</u> of the predicate. We thus have one single finite alphabet K_7; viz., the 7 symbols {1, 2, v, ,, p, ' , ⟶} from which all T.A's are constructed. It is completely trivial that representability in an arbitrary elementary dyadic arithmetic is equivalent to representability in one in transcribed notation. Thus an attribute is r.e. iff it is representable in some T.A. We use the terms "T.A. variable", "T.A. term", "T.A. predicate", "atomic T.A. formula" and "T.A. formula" to respectively mean "variable of some T.A.", "term of some T.A.", ..., "formula of some T.A."

We now construct our system U as follows. We extend K_7 to an alphabet K_8 by adding one new symbol "*". To every T.A. whose axioms are $A_1, \ldots, A_k$ we wish to associate a unique string in K_8; this string shall be $*A_1*A_2*\ldots*A_k*$. Such a string B is called a <u>base</u> (after Post). By a sentence of U we shall mean a string of the form BX, where B is a base and X is a T.A. formula. Alternatively a sentence is an expression of the form $*A_1*A_2*\ldots*A_k*X$, where $A_1, \ldots, A_k$, X are T.A. formulae. The strings $A_1, \ldots, A_k$ are called the <u>components</u> of B. We call the above sentence <u>true</u> in U iff X is provable in that T.A. whose axioms are $A_1, A_2, \ldots, A_k$.

REMARK. We have presented U as a so-called <u>semantical system</u>, rather than as a <u>syntactical</u> system, in the sense that we have defined what it means for a sentence to be "true" without reference to its provability in any axiomatic system. Alternatively, we could present U as an axiomatic system as follows:

AXIOMS: All expressions of the form BX, where B is a base and X is a component of B.

RULES OF INFERENCE:

1) If X_1 is an instance of X then BX_1 is directly derivable from BX.

2) BX is immediately derivable from the two sentences BF_1 and $BF_1 \longrightarrow X$ providing F_1 is atomic.

The provable sentences of this axiomatic system are precisely the same as the "true" sentences of U as we have defined them. This axiomatic system though not an "elementary" formal system is nevertheless a formal system in the sense that its set of provable sentences is representable in an <u>elementary</u> formal system - we shall prove this shortly.

Representability in U. By a predicate H of U (not to be confused with a T.A. predicate) we mean an expression of the form BP, where B is a base $*A_1*A_2*\dots*A_k*$ and P is a T.A. predicate. We say that this H represents (in U) the set of all n-tuples $(i_1, \dots, i_n)$ [of dyadic numerals] such that $Hi_1, \dots, i_n$ is true in U -- i.e., such that $Pi_1, \dots, i_n$ is provable in that T.A. whose axioms are $A_1, \dots, A_k$. Thus H represents the very attribute in U that P represents in the T.A. associated with B. So clearly an attribute is representable in U iff it is r.e. It is in this sense that U is called a "universal" system for all r.e. attributes.

We let S be the set of all sentences of U and T the set of all true sentences of U. For any set W of words in K_8, we understand $\tilde{W}$ as the complement of W relative to K_8. In §8 we shall employ the dyadic Gödel numbering, as explained in §6. Thus X_0 is the dyadic Gödel number of X, and for any set W of expressions in K_8, W_0 is the corresponding set of Gödel numbers -- in particular T_0 is the set of Gödel numbers of the true sentences of U.

§8. THE RECURSIVE UNSOLVABILITY OF U

We now come to the central point of this chapter. The set T of true sentences of U is f.r. over K_8 and the corresponding set T_0 of Godel numbers is recursively enumerable -- we prove this in the appendix to this chapter. We now wish to prove a variant of Post's form of Church's theorem; viz. that the set T_0 is not recursive. To prove that $\tilde{T}_0$ is not r.e. we employ a variant of the famous diagonalization argument of Gödel.

Let X be a sentence of U and A be any set of numbers. We shall say that X is a Gödel sentence for A iff the following condition holds: Either X is true and its Gödel number is in A, or else X is false (not true) and its Gödel number is outside A. Stated otherwise: $X \in T \Longleftrightarrow X_0 \in A$.

We immediately note that there cannot exist a Gödel sentence for the set $\tilde{T}_0$ (i.e., for the set of all numbers which are not in T_0), for such a sentence would be true iff it were false. Therefore to prove that $\tilde{T}_0$ is not r.e. it suffices to show that for every r.e. set A there is a Gödel sentence for A.

For any string X in K_8, we define its norm or diagonalization to be the string XX_0 -- i.e., X followed by its own Gödel number (written in dyadic notation). We note that if H is a predicate of U of degree 1 then the norm HH_0 of H is a sentence of U (this sentence intuitively expresses the proposition that the Gödel number of H lies in the r.e. set represented by H).

If n is a numeral, then n itself has a Gödel number n_0, and hence also a norm nn_0. By the isomorphism of our Gödel numbering relative to concatenation, we can at once assert that if n is the Gödel number of X then the norm of n is the Gödel number of the norm of X.

For any set A of numbers we define $A^{\#}$ as the set of all numbers whose norm is in A.

LEMMA. If A is r.e. so is $A^{\#}$.

PROOF. Let (E) be an elementary dyadic arithmetic in which A is represented by the predicate "A". Take a new predicate "G" (to represent the relation $g_0(x) = y$; cf. §6) and add the axioms of §6; viz.:

G1, 12
G2, 122
Gx, y ⟶ Gz, w ⟶ Gxz, yw .

Then take a new predicate "B" and add the one axiom:

Gx, y ⟶ Axy ⟶ Bx .

Then "B" represents the set $A^{\#}$.

Now we can prove:

THEOREM. For every r.e. set A there exists a Gödel sentence.

PROOF. Let A be r.e. Then so is $A^{\#}$ by the above lemma. Then $A^{\#}$ is represented in U by some predicate H. Then for every number n,

$$\begin{aligned} Hn \text{ is true } &\Longleftrightarrow n \in A^{\#} \\ &\Longleftrightarrow nn_0 \in A \ . \end{aligned}$$

Setting n = h, where h is the Gödel number of H, we have:

$$Hh \text{ is true } \Longleftrightarrow hh_0 \in A \ .$$

However hh_0 is the Gödel number of the sentence Hh. Therefore Hh is true iff its own Gödel number is in A -- i.e., Hh is a Gödel sentence for A. Q.E.D.

As we have already remarked there cannot exist a Gödel sentence for T_0. Hence we at once have

THEOREM [After Post's form of Church's theorem]. The set T_0 is not recursive.

Discussion. Our proof above involves the famous diagonalization argument of Gödel stripped down to its bare essentials. It was our express purpose to accomplish this with use of a minimum of formal machinery. All the arithmetical apparatus used is explicit in the above lemma.

Our proof of the recursive unsolvability of the system U leaned strongly on the particular formalism of U and on the particular Gödel numbering used. In Chapter III we shall largely get away from this -- i.e., we shall give a very general definition of a universal system, and will show that all universal systems are in fact unsolvable.

APPENDIX

FORMAL REPRESENTABILITY OF T AND T_0

In this appendix we prove that the set T of true sentences of U is f.r. over K_8 and that T_0 is r.e. We shall represent T in an elementary formal system $\mathcal{U}$ over K_8. Several other attributes in $\underline{K_8}$ will be represented along the way; some we need for the representation of T, others we need for subsequent use. For the sake of perspicuity we are presenting a longer list of axioms than is necessary.

We first note that the implication sign of $\mathcal{U}$ is to be distinct from the implication sign of T.A.'s (transcribed elementary dyadic arithmetics). We could continue to use "$\longrightarrow$" to denote the implication sign of U; we prefer however to use "$\longrightarrow$" to denote the implication sign of $\mathcal{U}$ (since it will occur so frequently), and we shall now denote the implication sign of T.A.'s by "imp". Similarly we shall now use the ordinary comma for our punctuation sign of $\mathcal{U}$, and "com" for the punctuation sign of T.A.'s. Variables of $\mathcal{U}$ (not to be confused with T.A. variables) will be denoted by "x", "y", "z", "w", with our without subscripts. Predicates of $\mathcal{U}$ (not to be confused either with predicates of U or T.A. predicates) will be introduced as needed.

We now introduce the axioms of $\mathcal{U}$ in groups, first explaining what each newly introduced predicate of $\mathcal{U}$ is to represent.

N represents the set of numbers (dyadic numerals).

N1

N2

Nx $\longrightarrow$ Ny $\longrightarrow$ Nxy

Acc represents the set of strings of accents

Acc'

Accx $\longrightarrow$ Accx'

V represents the set of T.A. variables:

Accx ——> Vvx

P represents the set of T.A. predicates.

Accx ——> Ppx

Px ——> Ppx

t represents the set of T. A. terms.

Nx ——> tx
Vx ——> tx
tx ——> ty ——> txy

F_o represents the set of atomic T.A. formulae.

Accx ——> ty ——> $F_o$pxy
F_ox ——> ty ——> $F_o$px com y

F represents the set of T.A. formulae.

F_ox ——> Fx
F_ox ——> Fy ——> Fx imp y

dv represents the relation "x and y are distinct T.A. variables".

Vx ——> Accy ——> dvx, xy
dvx, y ——> dvy, x

S represents the relation "x is any string (well formed or not) which is compounded from numerals, variables, predicates, com, imp; y is a variable, z is a numeral, and w is the result of substituting z for all occurrences of y in x (that is, all occurrences which are not immediately followed by more accents).

Nx ——> Vy ——> Nz ——> Sx, y, z, x
Vx ——> Nz ——> Sx, x, z, z
dvx, y ——> Nz ——> Sx, y, z, x
Px ——> Vy ——> Nz ——> Sx, y, z, x
Vy ——> Nz ——> S com, y, z, com
Vy ——> Nz ——> S imp, y, z, imp
Sx, y, z, w ——> Sx_1, y, z, w_1 ——> Sxx_1, y, z, ww_1

B represents the set of bases of U.

Fx ——> B*x*
Fx ——> By ——> B*xy

H represents the set of predicates of U.

Bx ——> Py ——> Hxy

Pt represents the relation "string x is part of string y"

Ptx, x
Ptx, yx
Ptx, xy
Ptx, yxz

C represents the relation "x is a component of the base y".

Fx ⟶ By ⟶ Pt*x*, y ⟶ Cx, y

T represents the set of true sentences of U.

By ⟶ Cx, y ⟶ Tyx
Bx ⟶ Ty, x ⟶ Fx ⟶ Sx, y_1, z, w ⟶ Tyw
Txy ⟶ Txy imp z ⟶ Fy imp z ⟶ F_0y ⟶ Txz

This concludes the construction of the system $\mathcal{U}$ in which T is represented. To represent T_0 over {1, 2}, just take all the above axioms and replace each symbol of K_8 by its dyadic Gödel number.

CHAPTER II: FORMAL REPRESENTABILITY AND RECURSIVE ENUMERABILITY

In this chapter we lay the groundwork for the remainder of this study. The results of #A are needed for Chapter III; Section #B is needed for Chapter IV. The results of #C, though not actually needed for our further development of recursive function theory, are of some independent interest and are useful in certain metamathematical applications.

§0. SOME PRELIMINARY PRINCIPLES

(a) Common Representability. Let (E_1) and (E_2) be 2 elementary formal systems over a common alphabet K. We shall call them independent iff they contain no common predicates. By $(E_1) \cup (E_2)$ we mean the E.F.S. over K whose axioms are those of (E_1) together with those of (E_2). Clearly every theorem of (E_1) and of (E_2) is again a theorem of $(E_1) \cup (E_2)$. And it is easy to verify that if (E_1) and (E_2) are independent, then every theorem of $(E_1) \cup (E_2)$ is provable in either (E_1) or (E_2) alone. Hence if (E_1) and (E_2) are independent then the representable attributes of $(E_1) \cup (E_2)$ are those of (E_1) and (E_2) alone. Similarly, if $(E_1), (E_2), \ldots, (E_n)$ are mutually independent, then the representable attributes of $(E_1) \cup (E_2) \ldots \cup (E_n)$ are those of each of $(E_1), \ldots, (E_n)$ alone.

PROPOSITION 1. If $W_1, W_2, \ldots, W_n$ are attributes in K which are f.r. over K, then they can all be represented in a common E.F.S. over K.

PROOF. Let $W_1, \ldots, W_n$ be represented in respective systems $(E_1), \ldots, (E_n)$ over K. Since we are assuming an unlimited stock of symbols at our disposal which we can use as predicates, then we can construct $(E_1), \ldots, (E_n)$ so as to contain no common predicates -- i.e., so as to be mutually independent. Then $W_1, \ldots, W_n$ are all represented in $(E_1) \cup \ldots (E_n)$.

(b) Improper Variables [For use in #C]. A device which will

sometimes reduce the number of axioms needed for the formal representation of attributes is the following: In addition to the variables $x_1, \ldots, x_n$ (which we might call proper variables) we take a finite number of signs $\alpha, \beta, \gamma, \alpha_1, \alpha_2,$ etc. which we call improper variables; these range over all strings in K including the null string. The rule of substitution now allows us either to substitute any string in K for an improper variable α or else to substitute the null string for α (i.e., to erase all occurrences of α). For the proper variables of course, only proper (i.e., non-null) strings may be substituted.

As an example, suppose we wish to represent the relation "string X is part of string Y". This relation is represented by "P" in the following system (whose variables are all proper):

$$Px,\ x$$
$$Px,\ xy$$
$$Px,\ yx$$
$$Px,\ zxy\ .$$

However, the system can be shortened by taking the improper variables α and β and the proper variables x and the one axiom: Px, $\alpha x\beta$.[1]

PROPOSITION 2. Any attribute which is representable in a system (E_1) over K using improper variables (as well perhaps as proper ones) is representable in a system (E_2) over K which uses proper variables exclusively.

PROOF. We construct (E_2) as follows: Replace each axiom A of (E_1) containing r improper variables by the 2^r axioms obtained by replacing some or all (or none) of the improper variables by proper variables, and deleting the rest. The provable sentences of (E_2) are precisely those of (E_1). Hence the representable attributes of (E_2) are the same as those of (E_1).

#A. CLOSURE PROPERTIES

In Chapter III our results on undecidability will be deduced from a few simple closure properties of the collection of all recursively enumerable attributes. These closure properties will be established in this section. As we are at it, we will show these closure properties to hold for the collection of all attributes in K which are f.r. over K (where

[1] The variables used in the productions of Post are all improper. We could have used improper variables exclusively for elementary formal systems, but again such systems would in general require more axioms than the joint use of proper and improper variables.

K is any fixed alphabet). [The latter will find additional applications in #C.]

§1. CLOSURE UNDER EXISTENTIAL DEFINABILITY

We wish to define what it means for an attribute W to be existentially definable from attributes $W_1, \ldots, W_n$. Loosely speaking, this means that W can be obtained from $W_1, \ldots, W_n$ by a finite number of operations of union, intersection, existential quantification and explicit transformations (i.e., permuting or identifying variables, putting in constants for variables or adding new variables). We now make this definition precise, first using the following preliminary definitions.

(a) Union and Intersection. Let W_1, W_2 be two attributes on a set S of the same degree n. By $W_1 \cup W_2$ we mean the relation $W_1(x_1, \ldots, x_n) \vee W_2(x_1, \ldots, x_n)$ -- i.e., the set of all n-tuples $(x_1, \ldots, x_n)$ which are either in W_1 or W_2 (or both). By $W_1 \cap W_2$ we mean the relation $W_1(x_1, \ldots, x_n) \wedge W_2(x_1, \ldots, x_n)$ -- i.e., the set of all n-tuples which are in both W_1 and W_2.

We refer to $W_1 \cup W_2$ as the "union" of W_1 and W_2, and $W_1 \cap W_2$ as the "intersection" of W_1 and W_2 (just as is customarily done for sets). We might also add that we are (informally) using the symbols "$\vee$" and "$\wedge$" to respectively mean "or" and "and".

(b) Existential Quantification. If R is a relation $R(x_1, \ldots, x_n, y)$ of degree $n + 1$ $(n > 0)$, by E(R) we mean the attribute $(Ey) R(x_1, \ldots, x_n, y)$ -- i.e., the set of all n-tuples $(x_1, \ldots, x_n)$ such that for some element y, $(x_1, \ldots, x_n, y) \in R$. E(R) is called the existential quantification of R.

(c) Explicit Transformation. Let $x_1, \ldots, x_n$ be symbols which we call variables over S; let $\xi_1, \ldots, \xi_k$ each be either one of the variables $x_1, \ldots, x_n$ or an element of S. Let W be an attribute of S of degree k. By the attribute $\lambda x_1, \ldots, x_n W(\xi_1, \ldots, \xi_k)$ we shall mean the set of all n-tuples $(a_1, \ldots, a_n)$ of elements of S such that $(b_1, \ldots, b_k) \in W$, where each b_i is defined as follows:

(1) If ξ_i is a variable x_j, then $b_i = a_j$.

(2) If ξ_i is an element of S, then $b_i = \xi_i$.

As an example, let S be the set of positive integers. Then the relation $\lambda x_1, x_2, x_3 W(x_2, 5, x_3, x_3, 7)$ is the set of all triples (a_1, a_2, a_3) such that the quintuple $(a_2, 5, a_3, a_3, 7)$ is an element of W.

We say that $\lambda x_1, \ldots, x_n W(\xi_1, \ldots, \xi_k)$ is explicitly definable from W. We let $\Phi(x_1, \ldots, x_n; \xi_1, \ldots, \xi_k)$ be that operation which assigns to each W (of degree k) the attribute $\lambda x_1, \ldots, x_n W(\xi_1, \ldots, \xi_k)$; such an operation we term an <u>explicit transformation</u>.

We note that the degree of an attribute which is explicitly definable from W may be greater than the degree of W. For example, let W be a set (attribute of degree 1). We can certainly consider the set of all ordered pairs (x, y) such that $x \in W$; this is the attribute $\lambda x_1, x_2 W(x_1)$ of degree 2, which is explicitly definable from W (it is also the cartesian product $W \times S$).

Now let Σ be a collection of attributes of S of varying degrees. We say that Σ is <u>closed under existential definability</u> iff Σ is closed under the operations of union, intersection, existential quantification and all explicit transformations. For any attributes $W_1, \ldots, W_n$ in S we can speak of the <u>smallest</u> collection Σ_0 which contains $W_1, \ldots, W_n$ and which is closed under existential definability -- Σ_0 is simply the intersection of all collections Σ which contain $W_1, \ldots, W_n$ and and which are closed under existential definability. We say that any element of Σ_0 is <u>existentially definable</u> from $W_1, \ldots, W_n$. Alternatively, W is existentially definable from $W_1, \ldots, W_n$ iff there exists a finite sequence $(V_1, \ldots, V_k = W)$ such that each attribute of the sequence is either one of the W_i or is obtainable from earlier terms of the sequences by one of the operations of union, intersection, existential quantification or some explicit transformation.[1]

We remark that any condition which can be written down by using just names of $W_1, \ldots, W_n$; names of elements of S; variables ranging over S; the logical connectives "$\wedge$" and "$\vee$" [which respectively stand for "and" and "or"] and the symbol "E" (to denote existential quantification), determines an attribute which is existentially definable from $W_1, \ldots, W_n$. For example, let W consist of the set of all triples (x, y, z) which obey the condition:

$$[W_1(x, 13, x) \vee W_2(z)] \wedge (Ev)W_3(x, v) \quad .$$

To prove that W is existentially definable from W_1, W_2, W_3 we exhibit the sequence:

$$W_1$$
$$W_2$$
$$W_3$$

---

[1] We are using the term "existentially definable" in a more general sense than that of Julia Robinson [21]. She calls an attribute of numbers "existentially definable" iff it is existentially definable (in our sense) from the two relations: $x + y = z$; $x \times y = z$.

$$W_4 = \lambda x, y, z\ W_1(x, 13, x)$$
$$W_5 = \lambda x, y, z\ W_2(z)$$
$$W_6 = W_4 \cup W_5$$
$$W_7 = \lambda x\ (Ev)\ W_3(x, v)$$
$$W_8 = \lambda x, y, z\ W_7(x)$$
$$W = W_9 = W_6 \cap W_8 \quad .$$

Henceforth when we state that a certain attribute W is existentially definable from attributes $W_1, \ldots, W_n$ we shall content ourselves with just writing down the conditions for membership in W, rather than explicitly displaying the scheme as we did above.

THEOREM 1. The collection Σ of all attributes in $\underline{K}$ which are f.r. over K is closed under existential definability.

PROOF. We must show that Σ is closed under union, intersection, existential quantification and explicit transformations.

(i) Union. Let $W = W_1 \cup W_2$, where W_1 and W_2 are attributes (say of degree n) which are f.r. over K. By §0 we can obtain an E.F.S. (E) over K in which both W_1 and W_2 are represented, say by predicates P_1 and P_2. Take a new predicate P and add to (E) the axioms:

$$P_1x_1, \ldots, x_n \longrightarrow Px_1, \ldots, x_n$$
$$P_2x_1, \ldots, x_n \longrightarrow Px_1, \ldots, x_n \quad .$$

In this extended system, P represents $W_1 \cup W_2$.

(ii) Intersection. Instead of the above two axioms, add rather the single axiom:

$$P_1x_1, \ldots, x_n \longrightarrow P_2x_1, \ldots, x_n \longrightarrow Px_1, \ldots, x_n \quad .$$

Now P represents $W_1 \cap W_2$.

(iii) Existential Quantification. Let P represent the relation $R(x_1, \ldots, x_n, y)$ in (E). Take a new predicate Q (of degree n) and add the axiom:

$$Px_1, \ldots, x_n, y \longrightarrow Qx_1, \ldots, x_n \quad .$$

Then Q represents the relation: $(Ey)\ R(x_1, \ldots, x_n, y)$.

(iv) Explicit Transformations. Let $V = \lambda x_1, \ldots, x_n W(\xi_1, \ldots, \xi_k)$;

let P represent W in (E). Take a new predicate Q and add the axiom:

$$P\xi_1, \ldots, \xi_k \longrightarrow Qx_1, \ldots, x_n \ .$$

Then Q represents V.

This completes our proof of Theorem 1. We remark that for K the alphabet {1, 2}, Theorem 1 says that the collection of all recursively enumerable attributes is closed under existential definability.

APPLICATIONS

(a) Images and Inverse Images of Attributes Under Functions. Let W be a relation of degree n on S and let f be a function from S into S. By f(W) we shall mean the set of all n-tuples $(f(x_1), \ldots, f(x_n))$ such that $(x_1, \ldots, x_n) \in W$. By $f^{-1}(W)$ we shall mean the set of all n-tuples $(x_1, \ldots, x_n)$ such that $(f(x_1), \ldots, f(x_n) \in W$. As with the case of W a set, we respectively refer to f(W) and $f^{-1}(W)$ as the "image" and "inverse image" of W under f.

The attributes f(W) and $f^{-1}(W)$ are both existentially definable from W and f (i.e., from W and the relation $f(x) = y$), for let V_1, V_2 be these two attributes respectively. Then

(1) $V_1(x_1, \ldots, x_n)$ is determined by the condition:

$$(Ey_1, \ldots, y_m)[f(y_1) = x_1 \wedge \ldots \wedge f(y_n) = x_n \wedge W(y_1, \ldots, y_n)] \ .$$

(2) $V_2(x_1, \ldots, x_n)$ is determined by the condition:

$$(Ey_1, \ldots, y_m)[f(x_1) = y_1 \wedge \ldots \wedge f(x_n) = y_n \wedge W(y_1, \ldots, y_n)] \ .$$

(b) Diagonalization, Substitution, Composition. For any function f(x, y) we define the function $\vec{f}$ of one argument by the condition $\vec{f}(x) = f(x, x)$. It is obvious that $\vec{f}$ is explicitly definable from f, hence is certainly existentially definable from f.

For any relation $R(z_1, \ldots, z_n, x_1, \ldots, x_m)$ by $R_{i_1, \ldots, i_n}$ we mean the set of all m-tuples $(x_1, \ldots, x_m)$ such that $R(i_1, \ldots, i_n, x_1, \ldots, x_m)$. Thus $R_{i_1, \ldots, i_n}(x_1, \ldots, x_m) \Longleftrightarrow R(i_1, \ldots, i_m, x_1, \ldots, x_m)$. We say that $R_{i_1, \ldots, i_n}$ arises from R by substitution. It is again obvious that $R_{i_1, \ldots, i_n}$ is explicitly definable from R, hence existentially definable from R.

For any function $f(z_1, \ldots, z_n, x_1, \ldots, x_m)$ by $f_{i_1, \ldots, i_n}$

we mean that function of m arguments defined by the condition: $f_{i_1,\dots,i_n}(x_1, \dots, x_m) = f(i_1, \dots, i_n, x_1, \dots, x_m)$. Again it is obvious that $f_{i_1,\dots,i_n}$ is explicitly definable from f [i.e., the relation $f_{i_1,\dots,i_n}(x_1, \dots, x_m) = y$ is explicitly definable from the relation $f(z_1, \dots, z_n, x_1, \dots, x_m) = y$]. A particular important use is when $m = n = 1$. Then $f_i(x) \underset{df}{=} f(i, x)$.

Let $g_1, \dots, g_m$ each be a function of n arguments. We define the function $f \circ (g_1, \dots, g_m)$ as that function h satisfying the condition: $h(x_1, \dots, x_n) = f(g_1(x_1, \dots, x_n), \dots, g_m(x_1, \dots, x_n))$. We say that h arises from $f, g_1, \dots, g_m$ by <u>composition</u>. Although h is not explicitly definable from $f, g_1, \dots, g_m$ it is nevertheless existentially definable from $f, g_1, \dots, g_m$, for the relation $h(x_1, \dots, x_n) = y$ is determined by the condition:

$$(Ey_1,\dots,y_m)[g_1(x_1,\dots,x_n) = y_1 \wedge \dots \wedge g_m(x_1,\dots,x_n) = y_m \wedge f(y_1,\dots,y_m) = y].$$

(c) <u>Cartesian Products, Relative Products, Inverse</u>. For any sets $S_1, \dots, S_n$ the cartesian product $S_1 \times \dots \times S_n$ (i.e., the set of all n-tuples $(x_1, \dots, x_n)$ such that $x_1 \in S_1$ and ... and $x_n \in S_n$) is existentially definable from $S_1, \dots, S_n$ -- in fact definable from $S_1, \dots, S_n$ by means of explicit transformations and intersection. For if we let $W_i = \lambda x_1, \dots, x_n\ (x_i \in S_i)$, then $S_1 \times \dots \times S_n = W_1 \cap \dots \cap W_n$. The relative product $R_1 \mid R_2$ of two relations R_1, R_2 of degree 2 (i.e., the set of all ordered pairs x, y such that for some z, xR_1z and zR_2y) is clearly existentially definable from R_1, R_2. Finally the inverse (or converse) $\breve{R}$ of a relation $R(x, y)$ (i.e., the set of all ordered pairs (x, y) such that $R(y, x)$) is explicitly definable from R, hence is existentially definable from R.

From considerations (a), (b), (c) above, the following corollary of Theorem 1 is immediate.

COROLLARY 1. (a) If W and f are both f.r. over K so are $f(W)$ and $f^{-1}(W)$.

(b) If $f(x, y)$ is f.r. over K so is its diagonal $\vec{f}$. If $R(z_1, \dots, z_n, x_1, \dots, x_m)$ is f.r. over K then for any elements $i_1, \dots, i_n$ the relation $R_{i_1, \dots, i_n}(x_1, \dots, x_m)$ (as a relation of $x_1, \dots, x_m$) is f.r. over K. If $f(z_1, \dots, z_n, x_1, \dots, x_m)$ is f.r. over K, then so is the function $f_{i_1, \dots, i_n}$. The collection of all functions which are f.r. over K is closed under composition.

(c) The cartesian product $S_1 \times \dots \times S_n$ of sets f.r. over K

is again f.r. over K. The collection of all dyadic relations which are f.r. over K is closed under inversion and the operation of taking relative products.

We shall also need

COROLLARY 2. Let f be a 1 - 1 function which is f.r. over K; let W be any attribute in $\underline{K}$. Then W is .f.r. over K $\Longleftrightarrow$ f(W) is f.r. over K.

PROOF. If W is f.r. over K, so is f(W), by the above corollary. Suppose f(W) is f.r. over K. Then so is $f^{-1}f(W)$, again by Corollary 1. But since f is assumed 1 - 1, then $f^{-1}f(W) = W$. So W is f.r. over K.

§2. SOLVABILITY OVER K

THEOREM 2. The collection of all attributes which are solvable over K is closed under complementation, union, intersection and all explicit transformations.

PROOF. More generally let us show that for any collection Σ of attributes on a set S, which is closed under existential definability, the collection Σ^x of all attributes W such that W and its complement $\widetilde{W}$ are both in Σ, is closed under complementation, union, intersection and all explicit transformations. Theorem 2 will then be immediate from Theorem 1.

Complementation is trivial. As for union, let W, V be elements of Σ^x which are of the same degree; let $M = W \cup V$. Clearly $M \in \Sigma$. Also $\widetilde{M} = \widetilde{W} \cap \widetilde{V}$, and since $\widetilde{W}$ and $\widetilde{V}$ are in Σ (by hypothesis) then so is their intersection $\widetilde{M}$. Thus $M \in \Sigma$ and $\widetilde{M} \in \Sigma$ -- i.e., $M \in \Sigma^x$. This proves the closure of Σ^x under union. The proof for intersection is obviously dual (or indeed is immediate from union and complementation). As for explicit transformations, let $M = \lambda x_1, \ldots, x_n W(\xi_1, \ldots, \xi_k)$. Then $\widetilde{M} = \lambda x_1, \ldots, x_n \widetilde{W}(\xi_1, \ldots, \xi_k)$. Thus if M is explicitly definable from W, $\widetilde{M}$ is explicitly definable from $\widetilde{W}$. If now $W \in \Sigma^x$ then W and $\widetilde{W}$ are both in Σ, hence M and $\widetilde{M}$ are both in Σ -- i.e., $M \in \Sigma^x$. This concludes the proof.

COROLLARY. The inverse of any relation which is solvable over K is again solvable over K. For any relation $R(z_1, \ldots, z_n, x_1, \ldots, x_m)$ which is solvable over K and for any elements $i_1, \ldots, i_n$ of $\underline{K}$, the relation $R_{i_1, \ldots, i_n}$ is solvable over K. Similarly with functions. The cartesian product of sets which are solvable over K is again solvable over K. (we recall that $S_1 \times \ldots \times S_n$ is definable from $S_1, \ldots, S_n$

using just intersection and explicit transformations.)

THEOREM 2.1. The inverse image of any attribute which is solvable over K under a function which is f.r. over K is solvable over K.

PROOF. Suppose W is solvable over K and f is f.r. over K. Then W and $\tilde{W}$ are both f.r. over K. By Theorem 1, $f^{-1}(W)$ and $f^{-1}(\tilde{W})$ are both f.r. over K. But it is easily verified that $f^{-1}(\tilde{W})$ is the complement of $f^{-1}(W)$. Thus $f^{-1}(W)$ and its complement are both f.r. over K, so $f^{-1}(W)$ is solvable over K.

The following theorem is more in the character of a lemma; it will have applications in #C and in Chapter III.

THEOREM 2.2. Let $W_1 \subseteq W_2$, where W_1, W_2 are attributes in K̲; let W_2 be solvable over K. Then W_1 is solvable over K iff both W_1 and $W_2 - W_1$ are f.r. over K.

PROOF. (a) Suppose W_1 and $(W_2 - W_1)$ are f.r. over K. By hypothesis $\tilde{W}_2$ is also f.r. over K. Hence the union $(W_2 - W_1) \cup \tilde{W}_2$ is f.r. over K. But this union is $\tilde{W}_1$ (since $W_1 \subseteq W_2$). Thus $\tilde{W}_1$, as well as W_1, is f.r. over K -- i.e., W_1 is solvable over K.

(b) Conversely suppose W_1 is solvable over K. Thus W_1 and $\tilde{W}_1$ are f.r. over K. Also W_2 is f.r. over K by hypothesis. Hence $W_2 - W_1$ (i.e., the intersection $(W_2 \cap \tilde{W}_1)$) is f.r. over K. So W_1 and $(W_2 - W_1)$ are f.r. over K.

<u>Discussion</u>. Consider now all the results of #A for the case when K is the alphabet {1, 2} of the dyadic numerals. Theorem 1 then says that the collection of all r.e. (recursively enumerable) attributes is closed under existential definability -- i.e., closed under unions, intersections, existential quantification and all explicit transformations. Theorem 2 says that the collection of recursive attributes is closed under Boolean operations (complementation, union and intersection) and also under all explicit transformations. Theorem 2.1 says that the inverse image of a recursive attribute under an r.e. function is recursive. Theorem 2.2 says that if $A \subseteq B$ where B is recursive, A is recursive iff A and $B - A$ are both r.e.

In the next section we consider further closure properties of the collection of all r.e. attributes; these properties (unlike those of this section) will involve the <u>arithmetical</u> significance of the dyadic numerals.

#B. RECURSIVE ENUMERABILITY

§3. RECURSIVE ENUMERABILITY OF SOME BASIC ARITHMETICAL ATTRIBUTES

THEOREM 3. The relations "x is the successor of y" (i.e., $x = y + 1$), $x < y$, $x \leq y$, $x > y$, $x \geq y$, $x = y$, $x \neq y$, $x + y = z$, $x \times y = z$ are recursively enumerable.

PROOF. (a) The relation "x is the successor of y" is represented by "S" in the elementary dyadic arithmetic whose axioms are

$$S2,\ 1$$
$$S11,\ 2$$
$$Sx2,\ x1$$
$$Sy,\ x \longrightarrow Sy1,\ x2\ .$$

(b) Add to the above axioms:

$$Sx,\ y \longrightarrow Ly,\ x$$
$$Lx,\ y \longrightarrow Ly,\ z \longrightarrow Lx,\ z\ .$$

Then "L" represents the relation $x < y$.

(c) Add to the axioms of (a) and (b)

$$Lx,\ y \longrightarrow L'x,\ y$$
$$L'x,\ x\ .$$

Then L' represents the relation $x \leq y$. Since the relations $x < y$, $x \leq y$ are r.e. so are their inverses $x > y$, $x \geq y$.

(d) Add to the axioms of (a), (b), (c) the axioms

$$Lx,\ y \longrightarrow Dx,\ y$$
$$Ly,\ x \longrightarrow Dx,\ y\ .$$

Then "D" represents the relation $x \neq y$.

(e) The relation $x = y$ is represented by "I" in the system

$$Ix,\ x\ .$$

(f) Add to the axioms of (a) the axioms

$$Sy,\ x \longrightarrow Ax,\ 1,\ y$$
$$Sy,\ w \longrightarrow A(x,\ w,\ v) \longrightarrow Sz,\ v \longrightarrow Ax,\ y,\ z\ .$$

Then "A" represents the relation $x + y = z$.

(g) Add to the axioms (a) and (f), the axioms

$$Mx,\ 1,\ x$$
$$Mx,\ w,\ v, \longrightarrow Av,\ x,\ z \longrightarrow Sy,\ w \longrightarrow Mx,\ y,\ z\ .$$

Then "M" represents the multiplication relation.

§4. RECURSIVE AND PARTIAL RECURSIVE FUNCTIONS

THEOREM 4. If the relation $f(x_1, \ldots, x_n) = y$ is r.e. then f is a recursive function (i.e., the relation $f(x_1, \ldots, x_n) = y$ is recursive).

PROOF. Let $R(x_1, \ldots, x_n, y)$ be the relation $f(x_1, \ldots, x_n) = y$. We are given that R is r.e.; we must show that $\tilde{R}$ is r.e.

Let (E) be an elementary formal system over {1, 2} in which "R" represents R and in which "D" represents the relation $x \neq y$ (this relation is r.e. by Theorem 3). Take a new predicate "P" and add the axiom:

$$Rx_1, \ldots, x_n, z \longrightarrow Dz, y \longrightarrow Px_1, \ldots, x_n, y \ .$$

Then "P" represents $\tilde{R}$.

We see, e.g., by Theorems 3 and 4, that the functions $x + y$ and $x \times y$ are recursive.

Partial Recursive Functions. Let $f(x_1, \ldots, x_n)$ be a function defined on some, but not necessarily all, n-tuples of numbers; let δf be the set of n-tuples on which f is defined. We call f a partial recursive function iff the relation $f(x_1, \ldots, x_n) = y$ is recursively enumerable.

Theorem 4 is obviously but a special case of

THEOREM 4.1. If f is partial recursive and if the domain δf of f is recursive then the relation $f(x_1, \ldots, x_n) = y$ is recursive.

PROOF. Again let $R(x_1, \ldots, x_n, y)$ be the relation $f(x_1, \ldots, x_n) = y$. Let (E) be an E.F.S. over {1, 2} in which "R" represents R; "D" represents the relation $x \neq y$ and "Q" represents the complement of δf. Take a new predicate P and add the axioms:

$$Rx_1, \ldots, x_n, y \longrightarrow Dz, y \longrightarrow Px_1, \ldots, x_n, y$$

$$Qx_1, \ldots, x_n \longrightarrow Px_1, \ldots, x_n, z \ .$$

Then P represents the relation $\tilde{R}$.

§5. FINITE QUANTIFICATION; CONSTRUCTIVE DEFINABILITY

For any relation $R(x_1, \ldots, x_n, y)$ by $E_F(R)$ we mean the set of all (n+1)-tuples $(x_1, \ldots, x_n, z)$ such that there exists a number y less than z such that $R(x_1, \ldots, x_n, y)$. The relation $E_F(R)$ will also be written:

$$\lambda x_1, \ldots, x_n, z(\text{E } y)_{<z}R(x_1, \ldots, x_n, y) ;$$

more briefly: $(\text{E } y)_{<z}R(x_1, \ldots, x_n, y)$. By $A_F(R)$ we mean the set of all (n+1)-tuples $(x_1, \ldots, x_n, z)$ such that for every y less than z, $R(x_1, \ldots, x_n, y)$. We also write $A_F(R)$ as $\lambda x_1, \ldots, x_n, z(\text{A } y)_{<z} R(x_1, \ldots, x_n, y)$ -- or more briefly as $(\text{A } y)_{<z}R(x_1, \ldots, x_n, y)$. We say that $E_F(R)$ arises from R by finite existential quantification, and that $A_F(R)$ arises from R by finite universal quantification.

THEOREM 5. (a) If R is r.e. so are $E_F(R)$ and $A_F(R)$.

(b) If R is recursive so are $E_F(R)$ and $A_F(R)$.

PROOF. Let R_1, R_2 be the respective relations $E_F(R)$, $A_F(R)$.

(a) The relation R_1 is existentially definable from the relation R and the relation $x < y$, for $R_1(x_1, \ldots, x_n, y) \longleftrightarrow (\text{E } z)[z < y \wedge R(x_1, \ldots, x_n, z)]$. Since R is assumed r.e. and the relation $x < y$ is r.e. it then follows that R_1 is r.e.

As for R_2, let (E) be an E.F.S. over {1, 2} in which "R" represents R and "S" represents the relation "x is the successor of y" (we already know that this relation is r.e.). Add the axioms:

$$R_2(x_1, \ldots, x_n, 1)$$ [1]

$$R_2(x_1, \ldots, x_n, z) \longrightarrow Sw, z \longrightarrow R(x_1, \ldots, x_n, z) \longrightarrow R_2(x_1, \ldots, x_n, w) .$$

Then "R_2" represents R_2; viz. $A_F(R)$.

(b) Obvious from (a), since $A_F(\tilde{R})$ is the complement of $E_F(R)$ and $E_F(\tilde{R})$ is the complement of $A_F(R)$.

Constructive Definability. We shall say that a numerical attribute A is constructively definable from attributes $A_1, \ldots, A_n$ iff it is obtainable from them by a finite number of applications of the following operations:

(1) Union
(2) Intersection
(3) Explicit Transformations
(4) Finite quantification (both existential and universal).
(5) Complementation.

We remark that if we started with the attributes $A_1, \ldots, A_n$ and their complements $\tilde{A}_1, \ldots, \tilde{A}_n$, then we would not need scheme (5). [This can be verified by an argument similar to the "prenex normal form"

---

[1] This condition is vacuously true, since there is no positive integer less than 1.

construction.]

If instead of (4) we allowed unbounded quantifiers, then the attributes thus obtained might well be termed "first-order definable from $A_1, \ldots, A_n$". An attribute A is called (after Gödel) "arithmetic" iff it is first order definable from the relations $x + y = z$ and $x \times y = z$. If A is constructively definable from plus and times, then we shall call it constructive arithmetic. It is immediate from Theorems 2 and 5 that all constructive arithmetic attributes are recursive.

A collection Σ of r.e. attributes is called a basis (for the r.e. attributes) iff every r.e. attribute is an existential quantification of some element of Σ. We shall also call a collection Σ_0 of r.e. attributes a sub-basis (for the r.e. attributes) iff the collection Σ of all attributes which are constructively definable from Σ_0 forms a basis for the r.e. attributes. It follows readily from results of Gödel that the constructive arithmetic attributes form a basis for the r.e. attributes (stated otherwise, the relations $x + y = z$, $x \times y = z$ form a sub-basis); we shall prove this in Chapter IV. This result is of fundamental importance in the proof of the Gödel incompleteness theorem (as well as related results on undecidability) for mathematical systems in which plus and times are definable (cf. Supplement).

#C. TRANSFORMATIONS ON ALPHABETS; GÖDEL NUMBERING

In this section we show:

(i) If K is a sub-alphabet of L then an attribute W of $\underline{K}$ is f.r. over L iff it is f.r. over K;

(ii) Both the lexicographical and dyadic Gödel numberings are admissible (in the sense of Chapter I, §6);

(iii) Our definition of recursive enumerability (which involves the choice of 2 as a base) is not really dependent on the base chosen.

§6. EXTENSION OF ALPHABETS

For any E.F.S. (E) over K and for any extension L of the alphabet K, we define $(E)_L$ as that E.F.S. over L whose axioms are the same as those of (E) (in particular, $(E)_K = (E)$). Now, a predicate P of (E) does not necessarily represent the same attribute in $(E)_L$ as it does in $(E)_K$. However, given any E.F.S. (E) over K with predicates $P_1, \ldots, P_m$ it is always possible to construct an E.F.S. $(\bar{E})$ over K such that for every extension L of K, each P_i represents the same attribute in $(\bar{E})_L$ as it does in (E). We construct $(\bar{E})$ as follows:

Let $a_1, \ldots, a_n$ be the symbols of K; let $X_1, \ldots, X_r$ be the axioms of (E). Take a new predicate Q (which is to represent the set $\underline{K}$) and for each axiom X of (E) let $\bar{X}$ be the string $Qx_1 \longrightarrow \ldots \longrightarrow Qx_s \longrightarrow X$, where $x_1, \ldots, x_s$ are the variables which occur in X. We now define $(\bar{E})$ to be that system whose axioms are:

$$\begin{array}{l} Qa_1 \\ \vdots \\ Qa_n \\ Qx \longrightarrow Qy \longrightarrow Qxy \\ \bar{X}_1 \\ \vdots \\ \bar{X}_n \end{array}$$

Now let L be any extension of K. It is readily seen that Q represents $\underline{K}$ in $(\bar{E})_L$ and that each predicate P_i of (E) represents the same attribute W_i in $(\bar{E})_L$ as it does in (E). We thus have

PROPOSITION 3. Let K be a sub-alphabet of L and let W be an attribute in $\underline{K}$, which is f.r. over K. Then W is also f.r. over L.

§7. DYADIC GÖDEL NUMBERING

We let K be an alphabet $\{a_1, \ldots, a_n\}$ containing at least 2 symbols -- we can assume without any real loss in generality that these symbols are "1" and "2". We let D be the alphabet {1, 2} of the dyadic numerals (which we are assuming is a sub-alphabet of K) and we consider the dyadic Gödel numbering g of $\underline{K}$ as explained in Chapter I, §6. We let G be the set $g(\underline{K})$ -- i.e., the set of all numbers which are Gödel numbers of expressions of $\underline{K}$. We note that G is the set of all numbers which can be expressed as a concatenation of the numbers $12, 122, \ldots, 1\underbrace{22 \ldots 2}_{n}$. The set G is obviously r.e. (f.r. over D); it is represented by Q in that E.F.S. over D whose axioms are:

$$\begin{array}{l} Q12 \\ Q122 \\ \vdots \\ Q1\underbrace{22 \ldots 2}_{n} \\ Qx \longrightarrow Qy \longrightarrow Qxy \, . \, . \end{array}$$

For any E.F.S. (E) over K we define $(E)_0$ to be that E.F.S. over D whose axioms are obtained from those of (E) by replacing each symbol of K by its dyadic Gödel number. If P represents W in (E) it does not necessarily follow that P represents W_o in $(E)_o$. However if we first consider the system $(\bar{E})$ as defined in §6 and then take the system $(\bar{E})_o$, it is easily seen that in $(\bar{E})_o$, Q will represent the set G and that P will represent W_o. Hence if W is f.r. over K then W_o is r.e. Conversely suppose that W_o is r.e. Since W_o is f.r. over D then W_o is f.r. over K (by Proposition 3). Since $W = g^{-1}(W_o)$ and since the function g is f.r. over K (as shown in Chapter I) it then follows (by Theorem 1, Corollary 1 (a)) that W is f.r. over K. We thus have

THEOREM 6. Under the dyadic Gödel numbering g of $\underline{K}$, an attribute W of $\underline{K}$ is f.r. over K iff W_o is r.e.

Now we can prove:

THEOREM 7. Let K contain at least 2 symbols; let $K \subseteq L$ and let W be an attribute in $\underline{K}$. Then W is f.r. over $K \Longleftrightarrow W$ is f.r. over L.

PROOF. We can assume without any real loss of generality that D is a sub-alphabet of K. Order L so that the symbols of K occur at the beginning; let g_1 be the dyadic Gödel numbering of $\underline{K}$ and let g_2 be the dyadic Gödel numbering of $\underline{L}$. Thus g_2 is an <u>extension</u> of the function g_1 -- i.e., for any string X in K, $g_1(X) = g_2(X)$.

Now let W be an attribute in $\underline{K}$. We have:

(1) W is f.r. over $K \Longleftrightarrow g_1(W)$ is r.e. [By Theorem 6].

(2) W is f.r. over $L \Longleftrightarrow g_2(W)$ is r.e. [Again by Theorem 6].

But $g_1(W) = g_2(W)$ [since W is an attribute in $\underline{K}$].

Then, by (1) and (2), W is f.r. over $K \Longleftrightarrow W$ is f.r. over L.

COROLLARY. Any numerical attribute A which is formally representable (in dyadic notation) over some extension of the alphabet D is r.e. (i.e., f.r. over {1, 2}).

§8. SOLVABILITY

By $\underline{K}^{(n)}$ we mean the n-fold cartesian product $\underbrace{\underline{K} \times \dots \times \underline{K}}_{n}$. For any extension L of K, the set $\underline{K}$ is solvable over L (cf. Chapter I, §3, Example d) hence $\underline{K}^{(n)}$ is solvable over L, by Theorem 2, Corollary 1 (3rd part).

THEOREM 8. Let $K \subseteq L$ and W be an attribute of $\underline{K}$ of degree n.

(a) If W is solvable over K, W is solvable over L.

(b) If W is solvable over L then W is solvable over K, providing K contains at least 2 symbols.

PROOF. We have just seen that $\underline{K}^{(n)}$ is solvable over L. Hence by Theorem 2.2, W is solvable over L iff both W and $\underline{K}^{(n)}$ - W are f.r. over L.

(a) Suppose W is solvable over K. Then W and $\underline{K}^{(n)}$ - W are both f.r. over K. Hence W and $\underline{K}^{(n)}$ - W are both f.r. over L (by Proposition 1, Corollary 1). Hence W is solvable over L by Theorem 2.2.

(b) Suppose W and $\underline{K}^{n}$ - W are both f.r. over L, and K contains at least 2 symbols. Then W and $\underline{K}^{n}$ - W are both f.r. over K (by Theorem 7). Hence W is solvable over K (again by Theorem 2.2).

§9. LEXICOGRAPHICAL ORDERING; n-ADIC REPRESENTATION OF NUMBERS

Let K be an alphabet of n symbols $a_1, a_2, \ldots, a_n$ $[n \geq 2]$ and let $X_1, X_2, \ldots, X_i, \ldots$ be the sequence of all strings in K arranged <u>lexicographically</u> -- i.e., according to length, and alphabetically within each group of the same length. We define the function S, from $\underline{K}$ into $\underline{K}$, by the condition: $S(X_i) = X_{i+1}$. Thus $S(X_i)$ is the <u>successor</u> of X_i, in the lexicographical sequence.

We let K_1 be the set of all words in the first symbol a_1. For any positive integer i, we let $\underline{i}$ be a string of a_1's of length i. We define the function h by the condition: $h(X_i) = \underline{i}$. We note that h is a function from $\underline{K}$ <u>onto</u> $\underline{K_1}$. We now wish to prove that W is f.r. over K (=) h(W) is f.r. over K.

LEMMA. (a) The function S is f.r. over K.
(b) The function h is f.r. over K.

PROOF. (a) The relation S(x) = y is represented by P in that E.F.S. over K whose axioms are:

$$S\alpha a_1, \alpha a_2$$
$$S\alpha a_2, \alpha a_3$$
$$\vdots$$
$$S\alpha a_{n-1}, \alpha a_n$$
$$Sa_n, a_1 a_1$$
$$Sx, x' \longrightarrow Sxa_n, x'a_1 \quad .$$

[Here α is an improper variable; cf. §0.]

(b) Add to the above axioms:

$$Ha_1, a_1$$

$$Hx, y \longrightarrow Sx, x' \longrightarrow Hx', ya_1 .$$

Then H represents the relation $h(x) = y$.

PROPOSITION 4. W is f.r. over K $\Longleftrightarrow$ h(W) is f.r. over K.

PROOF. Since the function h is 1-1 and f.r. over K then result follows from Theorem 1, Corollary 2.

n-adic Representation of Positive Integers. By n-adic representation of the positive integers, we mean the following: We take n symbols $\Delta_1, \Delta_2, \dots, \Delta_n$ (called n-adic digits) as respective names of the positive integers 1, 2, ..., n. And we take any string $\Delta_{i_n} \Delta_{i_{n-1}} \dots \Delta_{i_o}$ as the name of the number $i_o + ni_1 + n^2 i_2 + \dots + n^r i_r$. [This was done in Chapter I for the special case n = 2.] Any string Δ in the Δ_i is called an n-adic numeral (except for n = 1, in which case we call it a unary rather than "unadic" numeral). We note that if we arrange the n-adic numerals lexicographically, then the position occupied by a numeral Δ is the same as the number designated by Δ in n-adic notation. Stated otherwise, if we consider the lexicographical Gödel numbering of all words in an n-sign alphabet K (cf. Chapter I, §6) then the lexicographical Gödel number of any string X can be obtained by substituting (in X) Δ_1 for $a_1, \dots, \Delta_n$ for a_n, and reading off the n-adic numeral thus obtained.

For each n, we let D_n be the alphabet of n-adic digits. It will be convenient to choose all symbols Δ_i so that for each n, $D_n \subseteq D_{n+1}$. [We could thus start with a denumerably infinite sequence of symbols: $\Delta_1, \Delta_2, \dots, \Delta_i, \dots$ and define D_n to be the alphabet of the first n symbols of the sequence.]

For $n \leq 9$, we can take $\Delta_1, \Delta_2, \dots, \Delta_9$ to be the usual figures "1", "2", ..., "9". For $n > 9$, the reader can invent his own symbolism.

For any numerical attribute A (i.e., attribute of positive integers, we let $A_{(n)}$ be the corresponding attribute of n-adic numerals.

THEOREM 9. For $n, m \geq 2$:

(a) $A_{(n)}$ is f.r. over $D_n \longleftrightarrow A_{(m)}$ is f.r. over D_m.

(b) $A_{(n)}$ is solvable over $D_n \longleftrightarrow A_{(m)}$ is solvable over D_m.

PROOF. (a) In Proposition 4, let K be the alphabet D_n. We note that $A_{(1)} = h(A_{(n)})$. Hence by Proposition 4, $A_{(n)}$ is f.r. over D_n iff $A_{(1)}$ is f.r. over D_n. Similarly $A_{(m)}$ is f.r. over D_m iff $A_{(1)}$

is f.r. over D_m. But since D_n and D_m each contain at least 2 symbols and one of the alphabets is an extension of the other, it is immediate from Theorem 7 that $A_{(1)}$ is f.r. over D_n iff $A_{(1)}$ is f.r. over D_m. Hence $A_{(m)}$ is f.r. over D_n iff $A_{(m)}$ is f.r. over D_m.

(b) Trivial consequence of (a).

COROLLARY. For any $n \geq 2$, $A_{(n)}$ is f.r. over D_n iff A is r.e. (and $A_{(n)}$ is solvable over D_n iff A is recursive).

PROOF. By Theorem 9, setting $m = 2$.

We might call a numerical attribute A "r.e. in n-adic notation" iff $A_{(n)}$ is f.r. over D_n. Theorem 9 then says that for n, $m \geq 2$, A is r.e. in n-adic notation iff A is r.e. in m-adic notation. Thus, as claimed in Chapter I, our definition of recursive enumerability is not dependent on the base n chosen, provided $n > 1$. Consider now the case $n = 1$. Let us say that A is r.e. in <u>unary notation</u> iff $A_{(1)}$ is f.r. over D_1 (a number i written in unary notation is simply a string of 1's of length i). Suppose now that A is r.e. in unary notation. Then $A_{(1)}$ is certainly f.r. over D_n (for any n), hence $A_{(n)}$ is f.r. over D_n (by Proposition 4, since $A_{(1)} = h(A_{(n)})$) is r.e. -- i.e., A is r.e. in n-adic notation. So if A is r.e. in unary notation it is r.e. in n-adic notation. The converse, however, we do not yet know. All we can say (again by applying Proposition 4) is that if A is r.e. in n-adic notation then $A_{(1)}$ is f.r. <u>over some extension</u> of D_1; this does not mean that $A_{(1)}$ is f.r. over D_1. However it follows from a result in Chapter IV; viz., that every r.e. attribute is the existential quantification of some constructive arithmetic attribute, that every r.e. attribute is indeed r.e. in unary notation. Assuming this result from Chapter IV, we argue as follows:

Let Σ_1 be the collection of all attributes which are r.e. in unary notation. We know (by Theorem 1) that Σ_1 is closed under union, intersection, existential quantification and all explicit transformations. It therefore remains only to show that Σ_1 contains the relations plus and times and that Σ_1 is closed under finite quantification. Well, the relation "x is the successor of y" is obviously r.e. in unary notation (even more simply than in dyadic notation); it is represented by "S" in that E.F.S. over {1} whose one axiom is Sx1, x. Then all the numerical attributes of Theorem 3 (which indicates + and ×) are f.r. over D_1 (the remaining axioms in the proof of Theorem 3 can be carried over intact, though they can actually be simplified in unary notation). Likewise Theorem 5 (a) goes through in unary notation. This completes the proof.

§10. ADMISSIBLE GÖDEL CORRESPONDENCES

In Chapter I we defined a Gödel numbering g of $\underline{K}$ to be admissible iff for every attribute W in $\underline{K}$ the following conditions hold:

(i) W is f.r. over $K \Longleftrightarrow W_o$ is r.e.

(ii) W is solvable over $K \Longleftrightarrow W_o$ is recursive.

Let g now be the lexicographical Gödel numbering of $\underline{K}$; let W be an attribute in $\underline{K}$; let $A = W_o$. If we replace the symbols $a_1, \ldots, a_n$ by the respective n-adic digits "1", "2", etc., then clearly W becomes $A_{(n)}$; it is hence trivial that W is f.r. over $K \Longleftrightarrow A_{(n)}$ is f.r. over D_n, and W is solvable over K iff $A_{(n)}$ is solvable over D_n. And since $A = W_o$, it follows from Theorem 9, Corollary 1, that W is f.r. over K iff W_o is r.e., and W is solvable over K iff W_o is recursive. So the lexicographical Gödel numbering of K is admissible. We thus have:

THEOREM 10. There exists an admissible Gödel correspondence from $\underline{K}$ onto (a-fortiori "into") the set N of positive integers. The lexicographical Gödel numbering is such a correspondence.

§11. FURTHER FACTS ABOUT ADMISSIBILITY [OPTIONAL]

*THEOREM 11. A necessary and sufficient condition for g to be admissible is that g possess property (i), and that G be recursive.

PROOF [optional]. (a) Suppose g is admissible. Now, $\underline{K}$ is certainly solvable over $\underline{K}$. Hence G, viz. $g(\underline{K})$ is recursive by property (ii).

(b) Suppose g has property (i), and that G is recursive. Let n be the degree of W. Now, since G is recursive, then $G^{(n)}$ must be recursive (by Theorem 2, Corollary, statement 4, reading "D" for "K"). Hence we have:

W is solvable over $K \Longleftrightarrow W$ and $K^{(n)} - W$ are f.r. over K

$\Longleftrightarrow W_o$ and $(K^{(n)} - W)_o$ are r.e.

$\Longleftrightarrow W_o$ and $(K^n)_o - W_o$ are r.e.

$\Longleftrightarrow W_o$ and $G^{(n)} - W_o$ are r.e.

[since $(K^n)_o = G^{(n)}$]

---

* Theorems preceded by "*" are optional.

$\Longleftrightarrow W_0$ is recursive (by Theorem 2.2, setting $K = D_2$).

Thus g has property (ii).

*COROLLARY 1. If g is <u>onto</u> N, then a sufficient condition for g to be admissible is that g possess property (i).

*COROLLARY 2. The dyadic Gödel numbering is admissible.

PROOF. Let g be the dyadic Gödel numbering. We again identify the positive integers with their corresponding dyadic numerals.

We know that g possesses property (i) (Theorem 6). It remains to show that G is recursive. We know that G is r.e. (cf. §7). So we must show that $\tilde{G}$ is r.e.

Let n be the number of symbols in K. Then G consists of all numbers (dyadic numerals) which either begin with 2, end with 1, contain more than one consecutive occurrence of "1", or more than n consecutive occurrences of "2". Thus $\tilde{G}$ is represented (in dyadic notation) by P in the following E.F.S. over D_2. (α and β are improper variables; cf. §0.)

$$P2\alpha$$
$$P\alpha 1$$
$$P\alpha 11\beta$$
$$P\alpha\underbrace{22\ldots2}_{n}\beta$$

#D. A BRIEF SUMMARY

Let us summarize those facts of this chapter which will be used most frequently.

THEOREM I. The collection of all r.e. attributes is closed under existential definability and finite quantification.

THEOREM II. The collection of all recursive attributes is closed under union, intersection, complementation, all explicit transformations, finite quantification, and contains the relations $x + y = z$ and $x \times y = z$.

THEOREM III. For each alphabet K there exists an admissible Gödel numbering $g : X \longrightarrow X_0$ onto the set of positive integers -- i.e., a numbering such that for any attribute W in <u>K</u>, W is f.r. over K iff W_0 is r.e. and W is solvable over K iff W_0 is recursive. The lexicographical Gödel numbering is such a correspondence.

CHAPTER III: INCOMPLETENESS AND UNDECIDABILITY

This chapter is devoted to a reconstruction, generalization and extension of arguments involved in the Gödel and Rosser incompleteness theorems, Tarski's results concerning the definability of the "truth" set of a system within the system itself, and results of Church, Rosser and Kleene concerning undecidability. As remarked in the Preface, the results of this chapter are presented in a purely abstract form which does not employ the apparatus of mathematical logic; the more concrete applications are developed in the supplement.

The central idea of this chapter is that of a <u>representation system</u>, which allows us to study representability in systems of highly diverse syntactical structures. All systems which we shall be interested in possess at least the following features. We first have a set E, the so-called "expressions" of the system. In applications to logistic systems, E will consist of genuine formal expressions (n-tuples of elements called "symbols"). But for purposes of this chapter, E can be a completely arbitrary denumerable set. Then we have a subset S, the so-called "sentences", and a subset T of S, the so-called "valid sentences". In application to semantical systems, T will be the truth set, and in syntactical systems, T will be the set of theorems. Then we have the important notion of "representing" a set A, of numbers within the system. How this is done varies with the formal peculiarities of the system, but this much they all have in common:

One singles out certain expressions (elements of E) called "predicate formulae" or "predicates", and to each predicate H, and each number n, we assign, under a certain mapping Φ, a sentence, which we will denote by "$H(n)$". We then consider the totality of all n such that $H(n) \in T$, and this set we say is the set represented by H.

The function Φ varies considerably from system to system, and our whole purpose is to get away from all entanglements with the formal peculiarities of particular systems, and to study representability relative to a completely arbitrary function Φ. In this way, we prove related facts about various systems in one fell swoop, thus avoiding repetition of basically similar arguments.

Let us consider some examples. The notion of representing number sets within recursive dyadic arithmetics was considered in Chapter I. Here the appropriate representation function Φ is obviously that function which assigns to each expression X and each number n the expression Xn -- i.e., X followed by (the dyadic numeral designating) n. This representation function Φ is, so to speak, syntactically quite simple, involving only the operation of concatenation. A less simple situation arises with arithmetical systems considered in the language of the first order functional calculus.[1] Here the "predicates" can be taken to be those well formed formulas which contain exactly one free variable, and the representation function Φ assigns to each predicate $F(x)$ and each number n the sentence $F(\bar{n})$ which results from $F(x)$ by substituting the numeral $\bar{n}$ for all free occurrences of the variable x (this mode of representation is applicable only to formulations of arithmetic in which for each number n there is a numeral $\bar{n}$ to designate n). This representation function Φ involves the more complex operation of <u>substitution</u> (of numerals for individual variables). A simpler representation function Φ, which accomplishes the same thing, was discussed in Tarski [32]; this function assigns to each predicate $F(x)$ and each number n the sentence $(A\ x)[x = \bar{n} \supset F(x)]$ (alternatively the sentence $(E\ x)[x = \bar{n} \wedge F(x)]$ could be used). A still simpler representation system (which accomplishes the same thing as a first order arithmetic) was provided by the present author in [24]. Here we took <u>class abstraction</u> rather than quantification as primitive. A predicate H is then a <u>class abstract</u> -- i.e., an expression of the form $(\lambda x)\, F(x)$ (read: "the set of x's such that $F(x)$"). We then defined the set represented by H to be the set of all numbers n such that $H\bar{n}$ -- i.e., H <u>followed by</u> the numeral n -- is in T. For this system we would define $\Phi(H, n)$ to be H followed by $\bar{n}$. This function Φ again only involves concatenation rather than substitution.

The last three examples concerned systems which contain numerals to designate numbers. An example in which this is not the case is the system A^{0} considered in Church [2]. This is again a formalization of arithmetic in the first order functional calculus. However, there are no individual constants to denote the natural numbers, but there are certain well formed formulas $Z_0(x)$, $Z_1(x)$, $Z_2(x)$ ... etc. which intuitively express the respective properties: $x = 0$, $x = 1$, $x = 2$, ... etc. We

[1] This and the succeeding examples do presuppose an elementary familiarity with mathematical logic. A fuller discussion is given in the supplement.

again take as our predicates the w.f.f.s with one free variable -- say "x" -- and we define $\Phi(F(x), n)$ to be the sentence $(A\ x)[Z_n(x) \supset F(x)]$.

The above collection of examples should illustrate some of the applications of the theory of representation systems which we are about to develop. We again emphasize that this general study allows us to treat the mathematically significant aspects of incompleteness and undecidability without getting entangled in the formal peculiarities of any one type of representation system.

#A. INCOMPLETENESS

§1. REPRESENTATION SYSTEMS

By a *representation system* Z we shall mean a collection of the following items:

(1) A denumerable set E of elements called *expressions* together with a 1 - 1 Gödel numbering g of E *onto* N. [No assumption as to the "effectiveness" of g need be made until we come to #B.]

(2) A subset S of E whose elements are called *sentences* of Z.

(3) A distinguished subset T of S whose elements are called *true*, *valid* or provable sentences or *theorems* of Z.

(4) A second distinguished subset R of S whose elements are called *refutable* or *contra-valid* sentences of Z. [In application to systems in mathematical logic which contain negation, R will be the set of all sentences whose negation is provable in Z.]

(5) A set $\mathscr{P}$ of elements of E called (unary) *predicates*.

(6) A mapping Φ from $E \times N$ into E -- i.e., a function which assigns to each expression X and each positive integer n a unique expression $\Phi(X, n)$, which we abbreviate X(n) or even Xn. This function -- which we call the "representation function" of Z -- is required to have the property that for every predicate H and every number n, the expression Hn (i.e., $\Phi(H, n)$) must be a *sentence* (element of S).

We shall think of Z as the ordered sextuple $(E, S, T, R, \mathscr{P}, \Phi)$. [The ordering of T and R is important; in §7 we shall also consider the representation system Z obtained by interchanging the roles of T and R.] In certain contexts we shall use the letter "Q" rather than "Z" to denote a representation system. The fact is that in several of our definitions and theorems the set R plays no part; it is in these contexts that "Q" will be used instead of "Z" to emphasize the fact. Indeed if we think of "Q" as denoting the simpler structure (E, S, T, $\mathscr{P}$, Φ), all results remain valid.

Representability. We let H be a predicate of a representation system Q (either with or without the set R) and W be a set of expressions of Q. We define H_W as the set of all numbers n such that $H(n) \in W$. In particular, H_T is the set of all n such that Hn is valid in Q. We say that H represents the set H_T in Q. Thus for any number set A, H represents A in Q iff for every number n:

$$n \in A \longleftrightarrow Hn \in T \qquad [\text{i.e., } A = H_T]$$

Relational Representation Systems. In the supplement we shall need the notion of representing relations as well as sets. By a relational representation system Z we shall mean a system like a representation system defined above, with the following modifications: The set $\mathscr{P}$ shall consist of a set of expressions called "predicates" together with a function assigning to each predicate a positive integer called its degree. The function Φ shall be a mapping which assigns to each expression X and each n-tuple $(a_1, \ldots, a_n)$ of numbers an expression $X(a_1, \ldots, a_n)$. If X is a predicate of degree n, then $X(a_1, \ldots, a_n)$ is required to be a sentence. For any predicate P of degree n and for any set W of expressions, P_W is defined to be the set of all n-tuples $(a_1, \ldots, a_n)$ such that $P(a_1, \ldots, a_n) \in W$. And we say that P represents the attribute P_T in the relational representation system Z.

§2. FIRST DIAGONALIZATION LEMMA; TARSKI'S THEOREM

For any expression X we let X_0 be its Gödel number (under g). And (as in Chapter I) for any set W of expressions of Q, we let $W_0 = g(W)$. For any number i we let E_i -- or X_i -- be that expression whose Gödel number is i. The expression $X_i(i)$ -- i.e., $\Phi(X_i, i)$ -- will be called the norm or diagonalization of X_i.[2] If X_i is a (unary) predicate, then its diagonalization is certainly a sentence. We shall always use the letter "H" to stand for a (unary) predicate, and "h" to stand for its Gödel number. Thus Hh is the diagonalization of H, and Hh is a sentence. Such sentences we call diagonal sentences. [Heuristically, Hh is supposed to express the proposition that the Gödel number of H lies in the set represented by H.]

For any set W of expressions we define the set W^* of numbers by the condition: $i \in W^* \Longleftrightarrow X_i(i) \in W$. Thus W^* is the set of Gödel

---

[2] This terminology is from [23]. [A special case was used in Chapter I.]

numbers of all those expressions whose diagonalization is in W.

Complementation. For any set W of expressions, we let $\widetilde{W}$ be the complement of W within E. For any set A of numbers, we let $\widetilde{A}$ be the complement of A within N. The following facts are trivial:

(a) $\widetilde{(W_o)} = (\widetilde{W})_o$

(b) $\widetilde{(W^*)} = (\widetilde{W})^*$

(c) $H_{\widetilde{W}} = \widetilde{H}_W$

(a) is immediate from the fact that g is 1 - 1 from E onto all of N. As for (b), take any number n. Then

$$n \in \widetilde{W^*} \iff n \notin W^*$$
$$\iff X_n(n) \notin W$$
$$\iff X_n(n) \in \widetilde{W}$$
$$\iff n \in (\widetilde{W})^*$$

Thus $n \in \widetilde{(W)^*} \iff n \in (\widetilde{W})^*$, and since n is arbitrary, $\widetilde{(W^*)} = (\widetilde{W})^*$.

REMARK. Our assumption that g is onto N rather than into N (i.e., onto a subset of N) is one of convenience; all our results would be valid (some with a trivial modification) without this restriction. If g were into N rather than onto N, and if G were the set of all numbers corresponding to some element of E under g (i.e., if G = g(E)) then (a) and (b) above should be respectively read:

(a)' $(\widetilde{W})_o = G - W_o$

(b)' $(\widetilde{W})^* = G - W^*$

Gödel Sentences. In this chapter, we shall always use the letter "W" to mean a set of elements of E.

As in Chapter I, we define a Gödel sentence for a set A of numbers as a sentence X such that $X \in T \iff X_o \in A$. We shall also call X a Gödel sentence for a set W of expressions iff X has the property:

$$X \in T \iff X \in W .$$

Thus X is a Gödel sentence for the set W of expressions iff X is a Gödel sentence for the set W_o of numbers.

The following lemma is a highly abstract reconstruction and generalization of various "diagonalization" arguments, used by Gödel, Church, Tarski and others, to establish results on incompleteness, undecidability and the impossibility of representing certain sets within certain systems. This lemma -- a special case of which was used in Chapter I -- shall be basic to our entire study; we shall refer to it as the "first diagonalization lemma".

LEMMA I [First Diagonalization Lemma]. A sufficient condition for the existence of a Gödel sentence for W is that W^* be representable in Q. More specifically, if H is a predicate which represents W^* in Q, then its diagonalization Hh is an example of such a sentence.

PROOF. Suppose H represents W^* in Q. Then for any number n, $Hn \in T \Longleftrightarrow n \in W^*$ [by definition of representability]. Setting $n = h$, where h is the Gödel number of H, we have:

$$Hh \in T \Longleftrightarrow h \in W^*$$

$$\Longleftrightarrow Hh \in W .$$

Hence Hh is a Gödel sentence over W.

Consequence. Since there cannot exist a Gödel sentence for the set $\tilde{T}$, the diagonalization lemma at once yields:

THEOREM 1. The set $\tilde{T}^*$ (or $\widetilde{T^*}$, which is equal to it) is not representable in Q.

REMARKS. The diagonalization lemma is similarly provable under the weaker assumption that g is into N, rather than onto N. If G is onto a subset G of N then Theorem 1 should be modified to read "Neither of the sets $G - T^*$, $N - T^*$ is representable in Q."

Normality. We shall call Q a normal system iff it has the property that for every set W, if W_0 is representable in Q, so is W^*. Normal systems do in fact include the standard systems investigated by Tarski and Gödel. [Intuitively, normality of a system means that Gödel's diagonalization argument can be formalized within the system.]

[We remark that we could similarly define normality for the case that g is into N rather than onto N. In this case the system U of Chapter I is normal, by Lemma 1 - Chapter I. This lemma states that if A is r.e., so is $A^\#$. But for A a set of the form W_0, $A^\#$ is simply W^*.]

As an immediate consequence of Theorem 1 and the definition of normality, we see that in a normal system Q the set $\tilde{T}_0$ is not representable [for otherwise $(\tilde{T}_0)$ would be, hence by normality, $\tilde{T}^*$ would be representable, which is contrary to Theorem 1].

We shall call Q complemented iff the complement of every set representable in Q is again representable in Q. By the above paragraph and the definition of "complemented" we at once have:

THEOREM 1.1 [A rudimentary form of Tarski's theorem]. In a normal, complemented system Q, the set T_0 of Gödel numbers of the valid sentences of Q cannot be represented within Q.

[For semantical systems, the conclusion of the above theorem is sometimes paraphrased "truth within the system is not representable within the system"].

REMARK. In establishing the conclusion of Theorem 1.1 for specific systems, the bulk of the labor usually consists in establishing the normality of the system.

§3. CONSISTENCY AND COMPLETENESS; GÖDEL'S THEOREM

We define Z to be (simply) consistent iff $T \cap R$ is empty -- i.e., no sentence is both provable and refutable in Z. We call Z (simply) complete iff $T \cup R = S$ -- i.e., every sentence of Z is either provable or refutable in Z. A system which is both consistent and complete is called saturated; otherwise unsaturated. It is obvious that for any predicate H of Z the following conditions hold:

(1) If Z is consistent, $H_T \cap H_R$ is empty.
(2) If Z is complete, $H_T \cup H_R = N$.
(3) If Z is saturated, H_T is the complement of H_R.

A sentence X is called decidable in Z iff X is either provable or refutable in Z; otherwise undecidable. Thus $T \cup R$ is the class of decidable sentences, and the statement that Z is complete is equivalent to the statement that every sentence is decidable in Z. [The reader is cautioned not to confuse the meaning of the word "decidable", when applied to a particular sentence of a system with decidability of the system, in the sense of T being a solvable set of expressions.]

We note that for a consistent system Z, an undecidable sentence of Z is the same as a Gödel sentence for the set R. In fact the two statements "Z is unsaturated" and "there exists a Gödel sentence for R" are equivalent.

Gödel's Incompleteness Theorem in Miniature

THEOREM 2. If R^* is representable in Z then Z is inconsistent or incomplete. More constructively, if Z is consistent and if H is a predicate which represents R^* in Z, then its diagonalization Hh is an example of an undecidable sentence of Z. [A rudimentary form of Gödel's Incompleteness Theorem.]

PROOF. Immediate from the first diagonalization lemma, reading "R" for "W" and "Z" for "Q".

REMARKS. The above proof contains one of the two essential ideas behind Gödel's original incompleteness argument, shorn of all the complications involved in showing R^* to be representable in the particular system Z under consideration. The second essential idea involves the notion of "ω-consistency" and is dealt with in §3 of the supplement.

§4. COMPLETE REPRESENTABILITY AND DEFINABILITY IN Z

We have defined "H represents A in Z" to mean that for all numbers n, $n \in A \Longleftrightarrow Hn \in T$; i.e., iff $A = H_T$. We shall need the following notions of <u>complete representability</u> and <u>definability</u>.

We say that H <u>completely</u> (or <u>strongly</u>) represents A in Z iff for every member n:

(1) $n \in A \Longleftrightarrow Hn \in T$ -- i.e., $A = H_T$

(2) $n \notin A \Longleftrightarrow Hn \in R$ -- i.e., $\tilde{A} = H_R$.

These conditions of course imply:

(1)' $n \in A \Longrightarrow Hn \in T$ -- i.e., $A \subseteq H_T$

(2)' $n \notin A \Longrightarrow Hn \in R$ -- i.e., $\tilde{A} \subseteq H_R$.

If the weaker conditions (1)' and (2)' hold, then H is said to <u>define</u> A in Z.

We call a predicate H <u>numeralwise decidable</u> in Z iff for every number n, Hn is decidable in Z. Clearly if H is a predicate which defines some set in Z, then H is numeralwise decidable in Z.

Clearly if A is completely representable in Z then A is both representable and definable in Z. We shall frequently use the following proposition:

PROPOSITION 1. (a) If Z is consistent then every set definable in Z is completely representable in Z; a-fortiori representable in Z.

(b) If Z is saturated, then every set representable in Z is completely representable in Z.

(c) Hence for a saturated system Z, representability, complete representability and definability are all equivalent.

PROOF. (a) Suppose H is such that for every n

(1)' $n \in A \Longrightarrow Hn \in T$

(2)' $n \notin A \Longrightarrow Hn \in R$

We must now establish converse implications. Suppose $Hn \in T$. Then $Hn \notin R$ [by consistency]. Then $n \notin A$ is false [by (2)']. Hence $n \in A$. Thus $Hn \in T \Longrightarrow n \in A$. By analogous reasoning, $Hn \in R \Longrightarrow n \notin A$.

(b) Let $A = H_T$. Then $\tilde{A} = \tilde{H}_T$. If Z is saturated then $\tilde{H}_T = H_R$. Thus $A = H_T$, $\tilde{A} = H_R$, so H completely represents A.

From statement (c), we note that a sufficient condition for a system Z to be unsaturated is the existence of a set which is representable in Z but not definable in Z.

NOTE. For Z a relational representative system, the notions of complete representability and definability for relations are analogous to those for sets. For any predicate P and relation M of the same degree, P is said to completely represent M iff $M = P_T$ and $\tilde{M} = P_R$; P is said to define M iff $M \subseteq P_T$ and $\tilde{M} \subseteq P_R$. It is clear that Proposition 1 holds for relations as well as sets.

THEOREM 3. If Z is consistent then R^* is not definable in Z.

PROOF. Lemma I says that for any predicate H, $H_T \neq \tilde{T}^*$. Actually, it is more generally true (by similar reasoning) that for any set W, $H_W \neq \tilde{W}^*$. In particular $H_R \neq \tilde{R}^*$. Hence H cannot completely represent R^*. So if Z is consistent, then H cannot define R^* (by Proposition 1 (a).

§5. SEPARABILITY WITHIN Z; ROSSER'S THEOREMS

Gödel's incompleteness theorem (in the abstract form of Theorem 2) was based on the first diagonalization lemma. We now consider a more powerful lemma which will yield stronger incompleteness theorems (and subsequent undecidability theorems) due to Rosser.

Suppose W is a set of expressions of Q which is disjoint from T. By the first diagonalization lemma we know that a sufficient condition for the existence of a sentence which is outside both W and T is that W^* be representable in Q. We now prove the stronger fact:

LEMMA II [Second Diagonalization Lemma]. If H represents some superset A of W^* which is disjoint from T^*, then its diagonalization Hh is outside both W and T.

PROOF. Let H represent A; $W^* \subseteq A$; $A \cap T^*$ be empty.

Since H represents A, then for any number n,

$n \in A \Longleftrightarrow Hn \in T$.

Setting $n = h$, we have

$$h \in A \Longleftrightarrow Hh \in T$$
$$\Longleftrightarrow h \in T^* .$$

So $h \in A \Longleftrightarrow h \in T^*$. But A is disjoint from T^*, therefore $h \notin A$ and $h \notin T^*$. Since $h \notin A$ and $W^* \subseteq A$, then $h \notin W^*$. Thus $h \notin W^*$ and $h \notin T^*$ — i.e., $Hh \notin W$ and $Hh \notin T$. Thus Hh is outside both W and T.

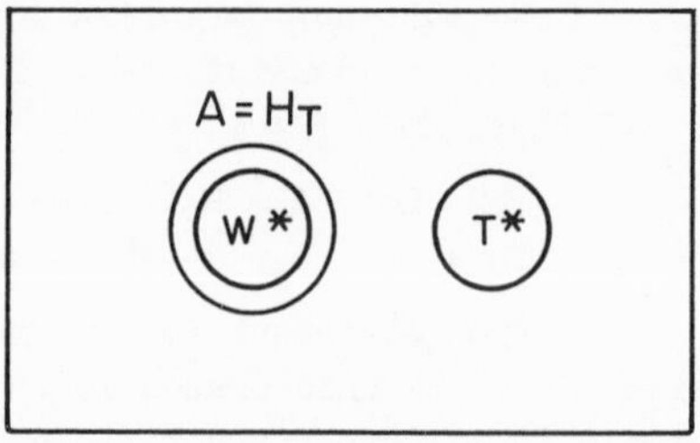

FIGURE 1

Weak separability within Z. Let A and B be disjoint sets of numbers. We will say that A is weakly separable from B within Q iff there exists a predicate H which represents some superset of A which is disjoint from B such a predicate H will be said to weakly separate A from B in the system Q. Lemma II says that if H weakly separates W^* from T^* in Q then Hh is outside both W and T. Taking W to be the set R, we immediately have:

THEOREM 4 [A rudimentary form of Rosser's Theorem].

A sufficient condition for Z to be incomplete is that R^* be weakly separable from T^* in Z. And if H effects this separation, then Hh is an undecidable sentence of Z.

REMARK. If A is a set disjoint from B and if A is representable in Q then A is obviously weakly separable from B within Q (since A is a superset of itself). Therefore Theorem 4 is indeed a strengthening of Theorem 2.

Strong Separability. Let A and B again be disjoint sets of numbers. We say that H strongly separates A from B within Z iff for every number n:

$$n \in A \Longrightarrow Hn \in T$$
$$n \in B \Longrightarrow Hn \in R .$$

More concisely: $A \subseteq H_T$ and $B \subseteq H_R$.

We say that A is strongly separable from B in Z iff there is a predicate H which strongly separates A from B within Z.

We note that the statement "A is definable in Z" is equivalent to the statement "A is strongly separable from $\tilde{A}$ in Z". In fact, H defines A in Z iff H strongly separates A from $\tilde{A}$ in Z.

PROPOSITION 2 (a). If Z is consistent and H strongly separates A from B, then H weakly separates A from B.

(b). Let $A_1 \subseteq A$ and $B_1 \subseteq B$. Then if A is weakly (strongly) separable from B within Z, then A_1 is respectively weakly (strongly) separable from B_1 within Z.

PROOF. Obvious.

By Theorem 4 and Proposition 2(a) we immediately have

THEOREM 5. Let H strongly separate R^* from T^* in Z, where Z is consistent. Then the sentence Hh is undecidable in Z.

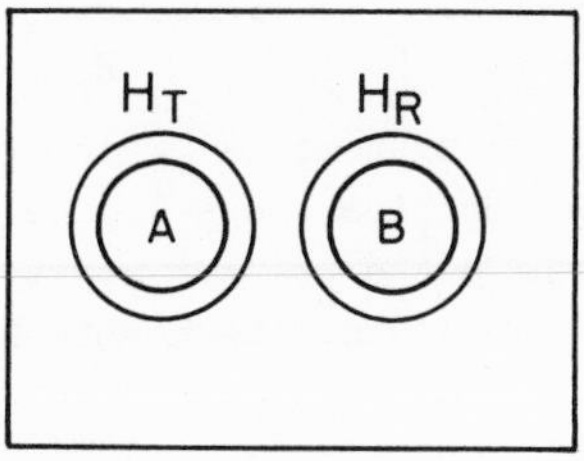

FIGURE 2

<u>A further application of Lemma II</u>. By using the second diagonalization lemma in place of the first, we obtain the following extension of Theorem 3; this extension will be important for our subsequent study of recursive inseparability (cf. Theorem 27).

THEOREM 6. If Z is consistent then no superset of R^* disjoint from T^* is definable in Z.

PROOF. Suppose: (i) T is consistent

(ii) H defines A in Z

(iii) $R^* \subseteq A$

(iv) A is disjoint from T^* .

We shall derive a contradiction.

By (i) and (ii), H completely represents A in Z. Thus $A = H_T$ and $\tilde{A} = H_R$. Then by (iii), $R^* \subseteq H_T$. And by (iv), $T^* \subseteq \tilde{A}$ — i.e., $T^* \subseteq H_R$. So $T^* \subseteq H_R$ and $R^* \subseteq H_T$ — i.e., H strongly separates R^* from T^* in Z. Then by Theorem 5, Hh is undecidable in Z. This means that $Hh \notin T$ and $Hh \notin R$, which means that $h \notin H_T$ and $h \notin H_R$. Thus H_R is not the complement of H_T. But $H_T = A$ and $H_R = \tilde{A}$, and $\tilde{A}$ <u>is</u> the complement of A. This is a contradiction.

§6. SYMMETRIC SYSTEMS

Let Z be a representation system $(E, S, T, R, \mathscr{P}, \Phi)$ and let $\breve{Z}$ be the representation system $(E, S, R, T, \mathscr{P}, \Phi)$. Thus $\breve{Z}$ is like Z except that the order of T and R is interchanged. Stated otherwise the provable sentences of Z are called "refutable" in $\breve{Z}$ and the refutable sentences of Z are called "provable" in $\breve{Z}$. We might call $\breve{Z}$ the dual system of Z. [The purpose in considering $\breve{Z}$ is to avoid repetition of some preceding arguments.] Since $\breve{Z}$ is a representation system then we can speak of representability, complete representability, definability and separability (both weak and strong) within $\breve{Z}$, just as we can within Z. Thus, e.g., H represents in $\breve{Z}$ the set H_R; H defines A in $\breve{Z}$ iff $A \subseteq H_R$ and $\tilde{A} \subseteq H_T$, etc.

The systems Z which we shall study in the supplement (which arise from theories whose logical basis includes the first order predicate calculus) have the property that for any predicate H there is another predicate H' (viz. the negation of H) such that $H_T = H'_R$ and $H_R = H'_T$. [This means that for every number n, Hn is provable in Z iff $H'n$ is refutable in Z and Hn is refutable in Z iff $H'n$ is provable in Z.] Systems having this property will be called <u>symmetric</u>. It is immediate that if Z is symmetric then representability in Z is equivalent to representability in $\breve{Z}$; likewise with "complete representability". Hence if Z is symmetric and consistent then a set is definable in Z iff it is definable in $\breve{Z}$. Also if Z is symmetric then strong separability within Z is equivalent to strong separability within $\breve{Z}$. [We might also note that if Z is symmetric, A is strongly separable from B within Z iff B is strongly separable from A within Z.]

Let us now consider a consistent symmetric system Z. By Theorent 1 (applied to the system $\breve{Z}$) $\tilde{R}^*$ is not representable in $\breve{Z}$; hence by symmetry (of Z) $\tilde{R}^*$ is not representable in Z. By Theorem 2, (again applied to $\breve{Z}$), if T^* is representable in $\breve{Z}$ then $\breve{Z}$ is incomplete (or what is the same thing, Z is incomplete). Hence by symmetry of Z, if T^* is representable in Z then Z is incomplete. Likewise by applying Theorems 3, 5, and 6 to $\breve{Z}$, and using the symmetry and consistency of Z, we can assert:

(i) T^* is not definable in Z;

(ii) If T^* is strongly separable from R^* in Z then Z is incomplete;

(iii) No superset of T^* disjoint from R^* is definable in Z. We thus have

THEOREM 7. Let Z be any consistent symmetric system. Then

(i) Neither $\tilde{T}^*$ nor $\tilde{R}^*$ is representable in Z.

(ii) Neither T^* nor R^* is definable in Z, nor is any superset of one disjoint from the other definable in Z.

(iii) If either T^* or R^* is representable in Z, or if either one is strongly (or even weakly) separable from the other in Z, then Z is incomplete.

§7. EXTENSIONS

We again emphasize that Gödel's method of proving incompleteness boils down to representing the set R^* (or T^*, if Z is symmetric);

Rosser's method consists rather of representing some superset of R^* disjoint from T^*. There is yet another method — due to Tarski — whose abstraction we now consider.

Let Z be a representation system (E, S, T, R, $\mathscr{P}$, Φ), let S', T', R' be respective supersets of S, T, R and subsets of E, let Z' be the representation system (E, S', T', R', $\mathscr{P}$, Φ). We call Z' an <u>extension</u>[1] of Z or Z a <u>sub-system</u> of Z'.

THEOREM 8 [After Tarski]. If R^* is representable in some consistent extension Z' of Z in which S = S' then Z is incomplete.

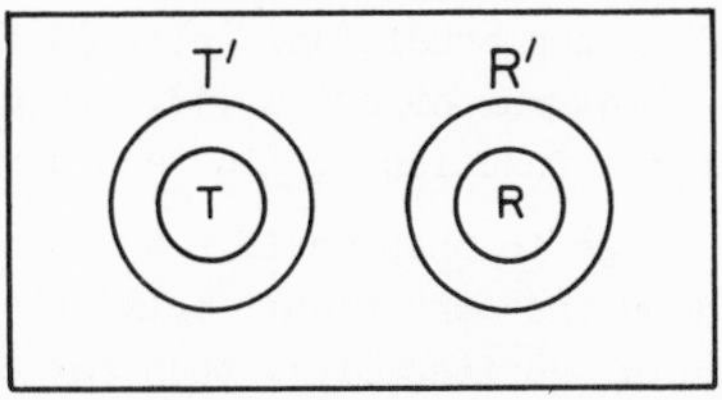

FIGURE 3

PROOF. Let H represent R^* in Z'. Then, by Lemma I (applied to Z'), Hh ε R <==> Hh ε T'. Since R' is disjoint from T' (by consistency of Z') and R ⊆ R', then R is disjoint from T'. Then Hh is outside both R and T'. Since T ⊆ T' then Hh is also outside T. Hence Hh is outside both R and T — i.e., Hh is indecidable in Z.

REMARKS. (1) It is likewise provable that if $\tilde{T}^*$ is representable in some consistent extension Z' of Z then Z is incomplete.

(2) Theorem 2 can be regarded as a special case of Theorem 8 in which Z' = Z.

This temporarily concludes our discussion of incompleteness. At this point the reader can turn to §1 - §4 of the supplement for a further discussion of the Gödel and Rosser incompleteness theorems and for an explanation of the role played by ω-consistency.

#B. UNDECIDABILITY

The results of #A do not employ any apparatus of recursive function theory. We now study representation systems from the viewpoint of undecidability; we still shall maintain the abstract spirit of #A. The results of this section will be established using only a tiny fragment of recursive function theory; viz. the closure of the collection Σ_0 of all r.e. (recursively enumerable) attributes under existential definability

---

[1] We are using here the term "extension" in the abstract sense of Uspenskij [33] rather than the more restricted sense of Tarski [32].

(this was established in Chapter II). Thus if we should consider an arbitrary collection Σ_0 whose elements we call "recursively enumerable", all results of #B and #C remain valid, providing Σ_0 has the above closure property. In this manner we obtain theorems which are actually more general than their explicit statements.

§8. SYSTEMS WITH AN "EFFECTIVE" REPRESENTATION FUNCTION

Associated with the representation function Φ of Q and the Gödel numbering g we now consider the <u>numerical</u> function $\varphi(i, j)$ defined by the condition: $\varphi(i, j) = k \longleftrightarrow \Phi(E_i, j) = E_k$. Thus $\varphi(i, j)$ is the Gödel number of $E_i(j)$. We now require that Φ be so related to g that the function φ is recursive.[1]

As in Chapter II, φ_i shall be that function of one argument defined by the condition: $\varphi_i(x) = \varphi(i, x)$. Since Σ_0 is closed under existential definability, then for every number i, φ_i is a recursive function of one argument. We also defined D(x) as the <u>diagonal</u> $\vec{\varphi}$ of φ — i.e., $D(i) = \varphi_i(i)$ — and we note that D is a recursive function. We also note that D(i) is the Gödel number of the diagonalization of E_i — i.e., $D(i) = g(E_i(i))$.

We recall (from Chapter II) that the inverse image of a r.e. set under a recursive function is r.e. and that the inverse image of a recursive set under a recursive function is recursive.

The following propositions will be used repeatedly:

P_1 - (a) $W^* = D^{-1}(W_0)$

(b) $H_W = \varphi_h^{-1}(W_0)$ [$H_W \underset{df}{=}$ Set of all n such that $H(n) \in W$;

$h \underset{df}{=}$ the Gödel number of H]

P_2 - (a) W_0 is r.e. $\longrightarrow W^*$ is r.e.

(b) W_0 is recursive $\longrightarrow W^*$ is recursive

P_3 - (a) W_0 is r.e. $\longrightarrow H_W$ is r.e.

(b) W_0 is recursive $\longrightarrow H_W$ is recursive.

PROOFS

(P_1) - (a) For any i:

$$\begin{aligned} i \in W^* &\longleftrightarrow E_i(i) \in W \\ &\longleftrightarrow g(E_i(i)) \in W_0 \\ &\longleftrightarrow D(i) \in W_0 \longleftrightarrow i \in D^{-1}(W_0) . \end{aligned}$$

[1] For a relational representation system Z we shall also require that for each n the function $f(x, x_1, \ldots, x_n) = g[E_x(x_1, \ldots, x_n)]$ be recursive.

Thus $W^* = D^{-1}(W_o)$.

(b) For any i:

$$\begin{aligned} i \in H_W &\longleftrightarrow \Phi(H, i) \in W \\ &\longleftrightarrow \varphi(h, i) \in W_o \\ &\longleftrightarrow \varphi_h(i) \in W_o \\ &\longleftrightarrow i \in \varphi_h^{-1}(W_o) \quad . \end{aligned}$$

Thus $H_W = \varphi_h^{-1}(W_o)$.

(P_2)-(a) W_o is r.e. $\longrightarrow D^{-1}(W_o)$ is r.e. [Since D is recursive]
$\longrightarrow W^*$ is r.e. [Since $W^* = D^{-1}(W_o)$]

(b) W_o is recursive $\longrightarrow D^{-1}(W_o)$ is recursive [Since D is recursive]
$\longrightarrow W^*$ is recursive

(P_3)-(a) W_o is r.e. $\longrightarrow \varphi_h^{-1}(W_o)$ is r.e. [Since φ_h is recursive]
$\longrightarrow H_W$ is r.e. [Since $H_W = \varphi^{-1}(W_o)$]

(b) W_o is recursive $\longrightarrow \varphi_h^{-1}(W_o)$ is recursive
$\longrightarrow H_W$ is recursive.

We shall refer to a set W of expressions of Q (or Z) as being "r.e." if W_o is a r.e. set of numbers; similarly with "recursive". We note that when E is the set of all words in an alphabet K, and g is an <u>admissible</u> Gödel numbering, then W is "r.e." iff W is f.r. over K and W is "recursive" iff W is solvable over K. We call Z a <u>formal</u> representation system iff S is recursive and T and R are both r.e. We call Z <u>decidable</u> iff T and R are both recursive. We again note that when E is the set of all words in an alphabet K and g is admissible that the above definitions of "formal" and "decidable" agrees with those of Chapter I.

§9. UNDECIDABILITY

Before stating our next theorems on decidability, let us note that the statement "T is not r.e." is equivalent to saying that for every r.e. subset W of T there is an element outside W but within T — a witness, so to speak, that W is not the whole of T. And to say that $\tilde{T}$ is not r.e. is equivalent to saying that for every r.e. set W disjoint from T, there is an element outside both W and T (a witness that W is not the whole of $\tilde{T}$).

THEOREM 9. If every r.e. set of numbers is representable in Q then $\tilde{T}$ is not r.e.

PROOF. Suppose $\tilde{T}$ were r.e. Then $\tilde{T}^*$ would be r.e., by

Proposition P_2. Then $\tilde{T}^*$ would be representable in Q (by hypothesis), contrary to Theorem 1. This completes the proof.

REMARK. The above proof is indirect. A more constructive version (closer to Gödel's original argument) is as follows:

The hypothesis implies (by P_2) that for any r.e. set W, W^* is representable in Q. Now let W be any r.e. set disjoint from T. Then W^* is representable in W. Let H be a predicate which represents W^*, and let h be its Gödel number. Then by the first diagonalization lemma, Hh is an example of an expression — in fact a sentence — which is outside both W and T (a witness that W is not the whole of $\tilde{T}$).

THEOREM 9'. If the complement of every r.e. set is representable in Q then T is not r.e.

PROOF. Suppose T were r.e. Then T^* would be r.e. (again by P_2). Then $\widetilde{(T^*)}$ would be representable in Q (by hypothesis), which is again contrary to Theorem 1.

[A more constructive version of the above proof runs as follows: Let W be any r.e. subset of T. Then W^* is r.e., hence $\widetilde{(W^*)}$ is representable in Q. So $\tilde{W}^*$ is representable in Q (since $\tilde{W}^* = \widetilde{(W^*)}$). Let H represent $\tilde{W}^*$. Then by the first diagonalization lemma, Hh is a Gödel sentence for $\tilde{W}$. Thus $Hh \in \tilde{W} \Longleftrightarrow Hh \in T$. But $W \subseteq T$, so $Hh \notin W$ but $Hh \in T$. Thus Hh is a sentence which is a witness to the fact that W is not the whole of T.]

REMARKS. Theorem 9 is obviously valid under the weaker hypothesis that every r.e. set <u>disjoint from</u> T^* is representable in Q. And Theorem 9' is valid under the weaker hypothesis that the complement of every r.e. <u>subset of</u> T^* is representable in Q.

We note that Theorem 9 says that if Q is strong enough so that all r.e. sets are representable within it, then Q, though possibly a formal system, cannot have a decision procedure. Theorem 9', on the other hand, says that if the complements of all r.e. sets are representable in Q then Q cannot even be a formal system, much less have a decision procedure.

The following theorem provides an even weaker condition that a system be undecidable.

THEOREM 10. If every <u>recursive</u> set of numbers is representable in Q, then Q is undecidable (more specifically, T is not recursive).

PROOF. Suppose T were recursive. Then $\tilde{T}$ would also be recursive. Then $\tilde{T}^*$ would be recursive, by P_2. Hence $\tilde{T}^*$ would be representable in Q (by hypothesis), which is again contrary to Theorem 1.

§10. NORMALITY

In #A we defined Q to be normal iff it has the property: For every set W, if W_o is representable in Q, so is W^*.

THEOREM 11. If the sets representable in Q are precisely those which are r.e., then Q is normal.

PROOF. Suppose W_o is representable in Q. We must show that W^* is representable in Q. Since W_o is representable in Q, W_o is r.e. by hypothesis. Hence W is r.e. Hence W^* is r.e. by P_2. Hence W^* is representable in Q, again by hypothesis.

§11. ADDITIONAL THEOREMS

THEOREM 12. If T is r.e. then every set A representable in Q is r.e.

PROOF. Suppose A is represented by H in Q. Then $A = H_T$. Since T_o is assumed r.e., then A is r.e. by P_3.

THEOREM 13. If T is r.e. and if every r.e. set is representable in Q, then Q is normal.

PROOF. The hypothesis and Theorem 12 together imply that the representable sets of Q are precisely those which are r.e. Hence Q is normal by Theorem 11.

THEOREM 14. If $\tilde{T}$ is r.e. then the complement of every set representable in Q is r.e.

PROOF. Let A be represented by H in Q. Thus $A = H_T$. Then $\tilde{A} = \tilde{H}_T$. It is easy to verify that $\tilde{H}_T = H_{\tilde{T}}$ (since g is 1 - 1 onto N). Thus $\tilde{A} = H_{\tilde{T}}$. Since $\tilde{T}_o$ is assumed r.e. then $H_{\tilde{T}}$ is r.e. — again by P_3. So $\tilde{A}$ is r.e.

THEOREM 15. If Q is decidable, then every set representable in Q is recursive.

PROOF. Suppose Q is decidable. Then T is recursive — i.e., both T and $\tilde{T}$ are r.e. Our theorem then follows from Theorems 12 and 14 (or alternatively from the second statement of P_3).

Theorems 12, 14, and 15 can be reformulated as follows:

THEOREM 16.

(a) If some set which is not r.e. is representable in Q then T is not r.e.

(b) If the complement of some non r.e. set is representable in Q then $\tilde{T}$ is not r.e.

(c) If some nonrecursive set is representable in Q then Q is undecidable.

DISCUSSION. Under the ordinary meaning of "recursively enumerable", Theorem 16-(b), together with the fact that there exists a recursively enumerable set which is not recursive, leads to an alternative proof of Theorem 9: Suppose that every r.e. set is representable in Q. Let A be a r.e. set which is not recursive. Then A is the complement of a nonrecursively enumerable set and A is representable in Q. Hence $\tilde{T}$ is not r.e. by Theorem 16-(b).

Similarly, Theorem 9' can be proved as a consequence of Theorem 16-(a) (providing we give "r.e." its usual meaning).

Of course, neither of these proofs remain valid if we consider an arbitrary collection Σ_0 which is closed under existential definability (since such a collection does not necessarily contain an element whose complement is outside the collection). On the other hand, our original proofs of Theorems 9 and 9' do remain valid under these more general conditions.

§12. UNIVERSAL SYSTEMS

We shall say that Q is universal iff Q is a formal system and every r.e. set is representable in Q. The system U of Chapter I is universal in this sense, (under the ordinary meaning of "r.e."). We proved the undecidability of U, appealing to certain peculiarities of the construction of U, and especially to the peculiarities of the dyadic Gödel numbering. The following theorem (a restatement of earlier results) is more general.

THEOREM 17. Let Q be *any* universal system. Then

(1) Q is undecidable

(2) Q is normal

(3) For any r.e. set W of expressions there is a Godel sentence for W.

(4) The set T_0 is r.e. but not recursive.

§13. UNDECIDABILITY AND INCOMPLETENESS

The following well known theorem establishes the crucial link between the undecidability results of Church and the incompleteness results of Gödel.

THEOREM 18. If Z is formal but undecidable, then Z is either inconsistent or incomplete.

PROOF. Suppose Z is formal and saturated. We show that Z is then decidable.

By hypothesis, S is recursive, T and R are r.e., $S = R \cup T$ and $R \cap T$ is empty. Since S is recursive, (E - S) is r.e. Hence $R \cup (E - S)$ is r.e. But $R \cup (E - S) = \tilde{T}$. Hence $\tilde{T}$ (as well as T) is r.e., so T is recursive.

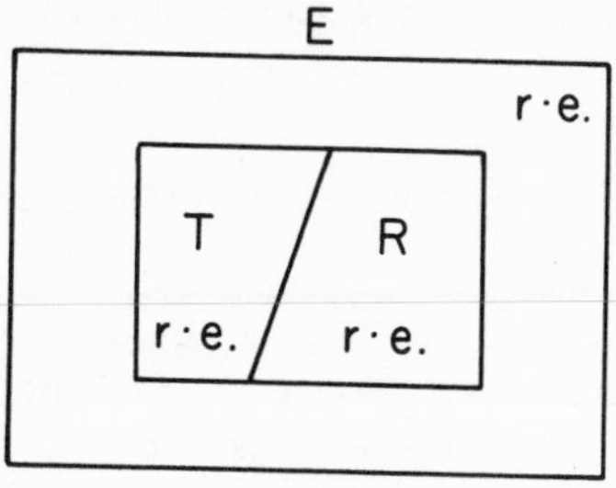

FIGURE 4

REMARKS. Actually, for a consistent formal system Z, the statement that T is not recursive is equivalent to the statement that for every r.e. set W disjoint from T there is a Gödel sentence for W. On the other hand, incompleteness merely means that there is a Gödel sentence for the particular r.e. set R. So, of course, undecidability (of a formal consistent system) is stronger than incompleteness.

From Theorems 10 and 18 we immediately have

THEOREM 19. If a formal system is strong enough so that every <u>recursive</u> set is representable in it, then it must be either inconsistent or incomplete.

REMARKS. The above theorem extends the well known form of Gödel's theorem — "A formal system in which every <u>r.e.</u> set is representable is inconsistent or incomplete". This result, though weaker than Theorem 19, can be proved in a manner which is more constructive: Suppose Z is formal and consistent and that every r.e. set is representable in it. Since Z is formal, then R^* is r.e. Hence R^* is representable in Z; let H represent it. Then the sentence Hh is undecidable in Z (by Theorem 2). (We might also note that this proof does not appeal to the fact that the set S of sentences is recursive, which was needed in Theorem 19 to pass from undecidability to incompleteness.)

Theorem 19 means that any consistent formal system must be inadequate in at least one of two ways: Either it is incomplete (and also undecidable) or else it is inadequate in an even worse sense, namely that it is so weak that even the recursive sets cannot all be represented in it. Such a system would not be adequate even for elementary number theory. To tell in which of the two senses a particular system is inadequate is a practical matter involving techniques peculiar to the system; this matter will be resumed in the supplement.

#C. UNDECIDABILITY AND RECURSIVE INSEPARABILITY

§14. DEFINABILITY IN FORMAL SYSTEMS

THEOREM 20. Every set definable in a consistent formal system is recursive.

PROOF. Let A be defined by H in Z, where Z is formal and consistent. Since Z is consistent, H completely represents A in Z. Thus $A = H_T$ and $\tilde{A} = H_R$. Since T and R are both r.e., by hypothesis of formality, then H_T and H_R are both r.e. (by P_3). So A and $\tilde{A}$ are both r.e. — i.e., A is recursive.

§15. EXTENSIONS

PROPOSITION 3. Let Z' be an extension of Z. Then

(a) If H defines A in Z then H defines A in Z'

(b) If H strongly separates A from B within Z then H strongly separates A from B within Z'.

PROOF. Statement (a) is but a special case of (b), setting $B = \tilde{A}$, so we prove (b). By hypothesis $T \subseteq T'$ and $R \subseteq R'$, hence it is obvious that $H_T \subseteq H_{T'}$ and $H_R \subseteq H_{R'}$. And by hypothesis $A \subseteq H_T$ and $B \subseteq H_R$. Hence $A \subseteq H_{T'}$ and $B \subseteq H_{R'}$ — i.e., H strongly separates A from B within Z'.

THEOREM 21. If every recursive set of numbers is definable in Z then every consistent extension[1] of Z is undecidable.

PROOF. Suppose every recursive set is definable in Z. Let Z' be any consistent extension of Z. Then by Proposition 3, every recursive set is definable in Z'. Then every recursive set is representable in Z' (since Z' is assumed consistent). Hence Z' is undecidable, by Theorem 10.

COROLLARY. If every recursive set is definable in Z then every formal consistent extension of Z is incomplete.

PROOF. By Theorem 21 and Theorem 18.

§16. RECURSIVE INSEPARABILITY

The notion of recursive inseparability plays a fundamental role in the modern approaches to incompleteness and undecidability. Two disjoint number sets A and B are called recursively separable iff there

---

[1] For "first order extensions" (cf. supplement) this theorem was proved by Hilary Putnam [18].

exists a recursive superset A' of A which is disjoint from B. [This implies that there exists a recursive superset of B — viz. $\tilde{A}'$ — which is disjoint from A, so the condition is symmetric.] A and B are called recursively inseparable (abbreviated "R.I.") iff they are not recursively separable. Equivalently, A and B are recursively inseparable iff for every disjoint pair (A', B') of r.e. supersets of A and B, there is a number outside both A' and B'.

We note that a single set A is recursive iff $(A, \tilde{A})$ is recursively separable (for the only possible disjoint pair of respective supersets of A and $\tilde{A}$ is $(A, \tilde{A})$ itself. Also, it is obvious that if A is recursively inseparable from B then the same holds for any disjoint pair of supersets (for any recursive separation of the larger pair is certainly a recursive separation of the smaller pair). Thus if we wish to prove a pair (A, B) to be R.I., we obtain a stronger result if we show some proper subset of A to be R.I. from some proper subset of B.

Now, let us consider a representation system Z. We shall refer to the sets T_0, R_0 as the nuclei of Z. We shall sometimes speak of the pair (T, R) as being recursively separable or inseparable, meaning more precisely that the pair (T_0, R_0) is respectively recursively separable or inseparable.[1] It is obvious that (T, R) is not R.I. iff there exists a recursive superset T' of T which is disjoint from R; such a superset T' gives rise to a consistent decidable extension Z' of Z, where S' (say) = E, R' (say) = (S' - T'). Conversely any consistent decidable extension Z' of Z induces a recursive separation of (T, R), since T' is then a recursive superset of T which is disjoint from R. Therefore the statement that every consistent extension of Z is undecidable is equivalent to the statement that (T_0, R_0) is R.I. Thus we can re-state Theorem 21 as

THEOREM 22. If every recursive set is definable in Z then the nuclei T_0, R_0 of Z are recursively inseparable.

§17. SEPARATION OF R.I. SETS WITHIN SYSTEMS

THEOREM 23. Let (A, B) be a pair of R.I. sets. Then

(a) If A is weakly separable from B within Q, Q is undecidable.

---

[1] If E is the set of all expressions of a finite alphabet K, and if g is an admissible Gödel numbering of K then it is immediate from the results of #C, Chapter II, that (T, R) is recursively separable iff there is a superset T' of T disjoint from R and solvable over K.

(b) If A is strongly separable from B within Z and Z is consistent, then its nuclei T_o, R_o are in turn recursively inseparable.

PROOF.

(a) Let H weakly separate A from B within Q. Then $A \subseteq H_T$ and H_T is disjoint from B. Since A, B are R.I. then H_T cannot be recursive. Hence Q cannot be decidable (for every set representable in a decidable theory is recursive, by Theorem 15).

(b) Suppose A is strongly separable from B within Z. Then A is strongly separable from B within every extension of Z (Proposition 3-(b)). Hence A is weakly separable from B within every consistent extension of Z (by Proposition 2-(a), #A). Then by (a) above, every consistent extension of Z is undecidable. Hence (T_o, R_o) is R.I. (since Z itself is assumed consistent).

§18. ROSSER SYSTEMS

By using the second diagonalization lemma in place of the first, we get the following extensions of Theorems 9 and 10.

THEOREM 24. If every r.e. set disjoint from T^* is weakly separable from T^* in Q, then $\tilde{T}$ is not r.e.

PROOF. Let W be any r.e. subset of $\tilde{T}$. Then W^* is r.e. Also W^* is disjoint from T^*, since W is disjoint from T. Hence W^* is, by hypothesis, weakly separable from T^* (in Q); let H effect this separation. Then by the second diagonalization lemma, Hh is outside both W and T. Thus if W is r.e. and disjoint from T, $W \neq \tilde{T}$ — i.e. $\tilde{T}$ is not r.e.

COROLLARY 1. If for every 2 disjoint r.e. sets A and B, A is weakly separable from B within Q, then Q is undecidable.

PROOF. Suppose T is r.e. Then T^* is r.e. Hence every r.e. set A disjoint from T^* is weakly separable from T^* in Q (this follows by hypothesis, setting $B = T^*$). Then by Theorem 24, $\tilde{T}$ is not r.e. Thus T and $\tilde{T}$ are not both r.e., so T is not recursive.

THEOREM 25 [Extends Theorem 10]. If every recursive set disjoint from T^* is weakly separable from T^* in Q, then Q is undecidable.

PROOF (By reductio-ad-absurdum). Suppose T were recursive. Then $\tilde{T}$ would be recursive, and $\tilde{T}^*$ would be recursive. Then by hypothesis $\tilde{T}^*$ would be weakly separable from T^*. Then (by the second diagonalization lemma) there would be a Gödel sentence for $\tilde{T}$, which is impossible.

COROLLARY. If for every two disjoint recursive sets A and B, A is weakly separable from B within Q, then Q is undecidable.

Rosser Systems. Many of the systems which arise in the literature possess the important property that for arbitrary disjoint r.e. sets A and B, A is strongly separable from B within the system. We shall refer to such systems as Rosser systems. The study of Rosser systems is one of the central objects of this work.

We note, by Proposition 3-(b), that every extension of a Rosser system is again a Rosser system.

THEOREM 26. Every consistent Rosser system Z has recursively inseparable nuclei T_0, R_0.

PROOF 1. Every formal consistent extension of a Rosser system Z satisfies the hypothesis of Theorem 24, hence is undecidable. Therefore Z has R.I. nuclei.

PROOF 2. We recall that a set A is definable in Z iff the pair $(A, \tilde{A})$ is strongly separable in Z, hence every recursive set is definable in a Rosser system. Result then follows by Theorem 22.

REMARKS. One way to construct an R.I. pair of r.e. sets is to take the nuclei of any formal consistent Rosser system. Another method, due to Kleene, will be considered in Chapter V. We remark that if we already had a recursively inseparable pair of r.e. sets available, then a third proof of Theorem 26 would be possible. For suppose every disjoint pair of r.e. sets is strongly separable in Z and that Z is consistent. Then take any pair (α, β) of r.e. sets which is R.I. Then (α, β) is strongly separable in Z. Then (T_0, R_0) is R.I. by Theorem 23-(b).

§19. RECURSIVE INSEPARABILITY OF THE DIAGONAL SETS T^*, R^*

In §2 we defined a diagonal sentence as the one of the form Hh, where H is a predicate and h is its Gödel number. For any set W we shall define $\vec{W}$ as the set of all diagonal expressions $X_i(i)$ which are in W. Let us consider the sets $\vec{T}$, $\vec{R}$, and their corresponding sets $(\vec{T})_0$ and $(\vec{R})_0$ of Gödel numbers. Clearly $(\vec{T})_0 \subseteq T_0$ and $(\vec{R})_0 \subseteq R_0$. Thus if we can show that $(\vec{T})_0$, $(\vec{R}_0)$ are R.I. we obtain a stronger result than if we show T_o, R_o to be R.I. (In general, for $A_1 \subseteq A_2$ and $B_1 \subseteq B_2$, the recursive inseparability of the smaller pair $(A_1 B_1)$ implies the recursive inseparability of the larger pair (A_2, B_2), but not conversely.)

We will soon see that the recursive inseparability of $(\vec{T})_o$, $(\vec{R})_o$ is implied by the recursive inseparability of T^*, R^*. We shall therefore focus our attention on the latter sets, which we term the diagonal sets of the system Z. We now wish to prove that if every recursive set is definable in Z and Z is consistent, then not only are the sets T_o, R_o recursively inseparable, but in fact the smaller sets $\vec{T}_o$, $\vec{R}_o$ are R. I. — in fact the diagonal sets T^*, R^* are R.I. To this end we introduce some new notions and establish some propositions which will have further applications in Chapter V.

Let (A_1, A_2) and (B_1, B_2) each be an ordered pair of number sets; let $f(x)$ be a function. We write $(A_1, A_2) \underset{f}{\rightarrow} (B_1, B_2)$ to mean that f maps A_1 into B_1 and A_2 into B_2 — i.e., that $f(A_1) \subseteq B_1$ and $f(A_2) \subseteq B_2$. We say that f maps the ordered pair (A_1, A_2) into the ordered pair (B_1, B_2). If $(A_1, A_2) \underset{f}{\rightarrow} (B_1, B_2)$, for some recursive function f, then we say that (A_1, A_2) can be recursively mapped into (B_1, B_2), and we write: $(A_1, A_2) \underset{Rc}{\rightarrow} (B_1, B_2)$. It is obvious that if $(A_1, A_2) \underset{f}{\rightarrow} (B_1, B_2)$ and if B_1 is disjoint from B_2 than A_1 is disjoint from A_2.

PROPOSITION 4. Let $(A_1, A_2) \underset{Rc}{\rightarrow} (B_1, B_2)$ and (B_1, B_2) be disjoint. Then if A_1, A_2 are R.I. (recursively inseparable) so are B_1, B_2.

PROOF. We prove the equivalent proposition: If (B_1, B_2) is recursively separable, so is (A_1, A_2).

By hypothesis, $(A_1, A_2) \underset{f}{\rightarrow} (B_1, B_2)$ for some recursive f. Now suppose (B_1, B_2) is recursively separable. Then there is a recursive superset S of B_1 which is disjoint from B_2. Then $f^{-1}(S)$ must be a superset of A_1 disjoint from A_2. And, since f and S are both recursive, $f^{-1}(S)$ is recursive. Hence A_1 is recursively separable from A_2.

COROLLARY. Let f be a recursive function; let A and B be disjoint sets of numbers. Then if (A, B) is recursively separable, so is $[f^{-1}(A), f^{-1}(B)]$. Stated otherwise, if $f^{-1}(A)$ is R.I. from $f^{-1}(B)$, then A is R.I. from B.

PROOF. Immediate from Proposition 4, since $(f^{-1}(A), f^{-1}(B)) \underset{f}{\rightarrow} (A, B)$.

PROPOSITION 5. For any sets W and V of expressions of Q:

(a) $(W^*, V^*) \underset{Rc}{\rightarrow} (\vec{W}_o, \vec{V}_o) \underset{Rc}{\rightarrow} (W_o, V_o)$

(b) $(H_W, H_V) \underset{Rc}{\rightarrow} (W_o, V_o)$ (for any predicate H of Z).

PROOF.

(a) Proposition P_1-(a)-§8 states that $W^* = D^{-1}(W_o)$, where D is the diagonal function. Actually, W^* is not only the inverse image of W_o under D, but is in fact the inverse image of the smaller set $\vec{W}_o$ under D. Thus $W^* = D^{-1}(\vec{W}_o)$ and $V^* = D^{-1}(\vec{V}_o)$. Hence $(W^*, V^*) \underset{D}{\rightarrow} (\vec{W}_o, \vec{V}_o)$. Since D is recursive then $(W^*, V^*) \underset{Rc}{\rightarrow} (\vec{W}_o, \vec{V}_o)$. And of course $(\vec{W}_o, \vec{V}_o) \underset{Rc}{\rightarrow} (W_o, V_o)$ (since $\vec{W}_o \subseteq W_o$ and $\vec{V}_o \subseteq V_o$).

(b) In §8, P_2-(b), we observed that $H_W = \varphi_h^{-1}(W_o)$. Thus $(H_W, H_V) \underset{\varphi_h}{\rightarrow} (W_o, V_o)$ and φ_h is recursive. This proves (b).

PROPOSITION 6. Let W and V be disjoint sets of expressions of Q. Then

(a) If (W^*, V^*) is R.I. so is $(\vec{W}_o, \vec{V}_o)$. (A fortiori if (W^*, V^*) is R.I. so is (W_o, V_o)).

(b) For any predicate H of Q:

(H_W, H_V) is R.I. $\Longrightarrow$, (W_o, V_o) is R.I.

PROOF. Immediate from Propositions 5 and 4.

THEOREM 27. Let Z be a consistent system in which every recursive set is definable. Then

(1) (T^*, R^*) is R.I.

(2) $(\vec{T}_o, \vec{R}_o)$ is R.I.

PROOF. Suppose T^* and R^* were recursively separable. Then there would be a recursive superset A of R^* disjoint from T^*. By hypothesis this recursive set A would have to be definable in Z. This is contrary to Theorem 6. This proves (i). Statement (ii) then follows by Proposition 6-(a).

COROLLARY 1. If Z is a consistent Rosser system, then (T^*, R^*) is R.I. (and likewise $(\vec{T}_o, \vec{R}_o)$).

<u>A constructive proof of the above corollary</u>. The proof of the corollary via Theorem 27 lacks a certain "constructive" feature, which it is possible to restore, under the stronger hypothesis that Z is a consistent <u>Rosser</u> system.

Suppose Z is a consistent Rosser system. Let A and B be respective r.e. supersets of R^* and T^*. We wish to exhibit a number outside both A and B. Well, by hypothesis there is a predicate H which strongly separates A from B within Z; this predicate then certainly separates the smaller pair (R^*, T^*) in Z. Then by Theorem 5, the sentence Hh is undecidable in Z; this means that h is outside both sets H_T and H_R. Hence h is outside the smaller sets A, B.

We have so far not been able to draw any stronger conclusion about the nuclei of a consistent Rosser system than about the nuclei of a consistent system in which all recursive sets are definable; in both cases we know that the nuclei are recursively inseparable. In Chapter V we shall see that for a consistent Rosser system, the nuclei have a stronger property known as "effective separability".

NOTE TO THE READER. At this point the supplement can be read through §5. It might also be well for the reader to then look at §6 - §8, which presupposes the fact (proved in Chapter IV) that plus and times forms a sub-basis for the r.e. attributes. [The results of §6 - §8 constitute, in fact, a large portion of the motivation for this theorem.]

CHAPTER IV

RECURSIVE FUNCTION THEORY

In this chapter we present a connected development of recursive function theory from the viewpoint of elementary formal systems. Sections #A and #B are completely independent. The results of #A are fundamental for all of Chapter V. The reader desirous of quickly seeing the applications of Chapter III to mathematical logic (as developed in the supplement) might wish to read #B before #A.

#A. EFFECTIVE OPERATIONS AND FIXED POINT THEOREMS

In Chapter II we showed that certain operations (e.g., union, intersection, existential quantification, finite quantification, explicit transformations) preserve recursive enumerability. One of the principal aims of this sections is to define what it means for an operation (on sets or relations of numbers) to be effective, and to show that the aforementioned operations are all effective in this sense. Speaking informally for the moment, an effective operation is one such that given any elementary formal system in which the arguments of the operation are represented, there not only exists an E.F.S. in which the value of the operation is represented (which merely says that the operation preserves recursive enumerability) but that such a system can be "effectively" found from the given systems. This definition is made precise in terms of indexing all r.e. attributes (cf. §1 and §2). [Roughly speaking, an index of an r.e. attribute A is the dyadic Gödel number of any predicate which represents A in the universal system U of Chapter I.] Preparatory to the study of effective operations, we need the Post-Kleene enumeration theorem (§1) and the "iteration" theorems, as developed in §3.

§1. ENUMERATION THEOREM

We return to the universal system (U) of Chapter I.[1] Let Ψ^n

[1] We are here calling this system "(U)" rather than "U" because "U" will be used in a different context.

be the set of all (n+1)-tuples $(X, x_1, \ldots, x_n)$ such that X is a predicate of (U) (of degree n) and $x_1, \ldots, x_n$ are numbers (dyadic numerals) such that $(x_1, \ldots, x_n)$ <u>satisfies</u> X — i.e., such that $X, x_1, \ldots, x_n$ is true in (U) (equivalently such that $x_1, \ldots, x_n)$ is in the r.e. relation represented in (U) by X). And let U^n be the set of all (n+1)-tuples $(x, x_1, \ldots, x_n)$ of positive integers such that x is the Gödel number of a predicate X which is satisfied by $(x_1, \ldots, x_n)$. Thus if x is not the Gödel number of a predicate of degree n, then $U^n(x, x_1, \ldots, x_n)$ is false. If x is the Gödel number of a predicate X of degree n, then $U^n(x, x_1, \ldots, x_n) \Longleftrightarrow \Psi^n(X, x_1, \ldots, x_n)$. We sometimes write "$U(x, x_1, \ldots, x_n)$" for "$U^n(x, x_1, \ldots, x_n)$", since it is obvious what the superscript n must be.

The relation U^n is obviously <u>universal</u> in the sense that for every recursively enumerable relation $R(x_1, \ldots, x_n)$ there is a number i; viz. the Gödel number of any predicate of the system (U) which represents R, such that $R(x_1, \ldots, x_n) \longleftrightarrow U^n(i, x_1, \ldots, x_n)$. We wish to prove that for each n the relation U^n is itself r.e. (Post-Kleene Enumeration Theorem, stated by Post, Kleene for a different universal relation).

THEOREM 1 (after Post-Kleene). For each n, U^n is r.e.

PROOF. (a) We first show that for each n the relation $\Psi^n(X, x_1, \ldots, x_n)$ is f.r. over K_8. We consider the E.F.S. ($\mathcal{U}$) over K_8 constructed in the Appendix to Chapter I. In this system "N" represents the set of numbers (dyadic numerals), "B" represents the set of bases, "Acc" represents the set of strings of accents and "T" represents the set of true sentences of (U).

For each n we extend ($\mathcal{U}$) to a system ($\mathcal{U}^n$) over K_8 as follows: We take a new predicate "H" of $\mathcal{U}$ and add the axiom:

$$Bx \longrightarrow Acc\ y \longrightarrow Hx\,\underbrace{pp \ldots p}_{n}y$$

Then "H" represents the set of predicates of (U) of degree n. Then we take a new predicate "L" of $\mathcal{U}$ and add the axiom:

$$Hx \longrightarrow Nx_1 \longrightarrow \ldots \longrightarrow Nx_n \longrightarrow Txx_1 \text{ com } x_2 \text{ com } \ldots \text{ com } x_n \longrightarrow Lx, x_1, \ldots, x_n.$$

Then "L" represents Ψ^n.

(b) For the reader familiar with #C of Chapter II, the recursive enumerability of U^n is virtually immediate from the formal representability of Ψ^n over K_8: Let g be the dyadic Gödel numbering of K_8. Then U^n is existentially definable from the relation Ψ^n and the relation $g(x) = y$, since $U^n(x, x_1, \ldots, x_n) \longleftrightarrow (EX)[g(X) = x \wedge \Psi^n(X, x_1, \ldots, x_n)]$. Thus U^n is f.r. over K_8, hence r.e. by Theorem

7, Chapter II.

For the reader not familiar with #C of Chapter II, we derive the recursive enumerability of U^n as follows: Let $(\mathcal{U}^n)_0$ be the E.F.S. over {1, 2} whose axioms are obtained from those of $(\mathcal{U}^n)$ (cf. (a)) by everywhere replacing each symbol of K_8 by its dyadic Gödel number. In this elementary dyadic arithmetic $(\mathcal{U}^n)_0$ the predicate L represents not the desired relation U^n, but rather the set of all (n+1)-tuples $(x, g(x_1), \ldots, g(x_n))$ such that $U^n(x, x_1, \ldots, x_n)$. To represent U^n itself over {1, 2}, we take two new predicates "G" and "P" and add to $(\mathcal{U}^n)_0$ the axioms:

G1, 12

G2, 122

$Gx, y \longrightarrow Gz, w \longrightarrow Gxz, yw$

$Lx, y_1, \ldots, y_n \longrightarrow Gx_1, y_1 \longrightarrow \ldots \longrightarrow Gx_n, y_n \longrightarrow Px, x_1, \ldots, x_n.$

In this system, "G" represents the relation $g_0(x) = y$ -- i.e., the set of all ordered pairs (x, y) of dyadic numerals such that $g(x) = y$ -- and "P" represents the desired relation U^n.

§2. INDEXING

By R_i^n we shall mean the set of all n-tuples $(x_1, \ldots, x_n)$ such that $U(i, x_1, \ldots, x_n)$. When no ambiguity can result, we shall often omit the superscipt n — e.g., we only need write "$R_i(x_1, \ldots, x_n)$" rather than $R_i^n(x_1, \ldots, x_n)$. Thus $R_i(x_1, \ldots, x_n) \longleftrightarrow U(i, x_1, \ldots, x_n)$. We call i an <u>index</u> of R_i. Clearly if i is the Gödel number of some predicate H of U of degree n, then R_i^n is the relation represented in U by H. If i is not such a Gödel number, R_i^n is empty.

Following the usual notation, for n = 1 we write "ω_i" rather than "R_i^1". Thus ω_i is that r.e. set whose index is i. We think of all r.e. sets arranged in the sequence $\omega_1, \omega_2, \ldots, \omega_i, \ldots,$ and Post's Enumeration Theorem [for n = 1] states that the set of all pairs (i, j) such that $j \in \omega_i$ is an r.e. relation.

§3. ITERATION THEOREMS FOR r.e. RELATIONS[1]

For any relation $M(z_1, \ldots, z_n, x_1, \ldots, x_m)$ and for any numbers $i_1, \ldots, i_n$ we let $M_{i_1,\ldots,i_n}$ be the set of all m-tuples

---

[1] The theorems of this section play the analogous role to the theory of r.e. relations as Kleene's S_n^m theorem [11] does to partial recursive functions. It is possible to derive the iteration theorems for relations as a consequence of Kleene's theorem for functions, but we believe it is simpler to proceed in the other direction (cf. discussion following Theorem 10).

$(x_1, \ldots, x_m)$ such that $M(i_1, \ldots, i_n, x_1, \ldots, x_m)$ [this was already explained in Chapter II].

THEOREM 2. For any recursively enumerable relation $M(z_1, \ldots, z_n, x_1, \ldots, x_m)$ there is a recursive function $\varphi(z_1, \ldots, z_n)$[2] such that for all numbers $i_1, \ldots, i_n$, $\varphi(i_1, \ldots, i_n)$ is an index of $M_{i_1,\ldots,i_n}$.

PROOF. Let (E) be a transcribed elementary dyadic arithmetic in which P represents M. Let $X_1, \ldots, X_k$ be the axiom of (E) and let B be the base $*X_1*X_2*\ldots*X_k*$. Let Q be a T.A. predicate which does not occur in (E), and for any numbers $i_1, \ldots, i_n$ let $Y_{i_1,\ldots,i_n}$ be the string

$$Pi_1, i_2, \ldots, i_n, x_1, \ldots, x_m \longrightarrow Qx_1, \ldots, x_m \ .$$

Let $(E)_{i_1,\ldots,i_n}$ result from (E) by adding the axiom $Y_{i_1,\ldots,i_n}$. We note that Q represents $M_{i_1,\ldots,i_n}$ in $(E)_{i_1,\ldots,i_n}$. We also note that $BY_{i_1,\ldots,i_n}*$ is a base corresponding to $(E)_{i_1,\ldots,i_n}$ and that the string $BY_{i_1,\ldots,i_n}*Q$ is a predicate of U which represents (in (U)) the relation $M_{i_1,\ldots,i_n}$. Hence the Gödel number of this predicate is an index of $M_{i_1,\ldots,i_n}$; let $\varphi(i_1, \ldots, i_n)$ be this Gödel number. It remains to show that φ is a recursive function.

Well, let b, p, q be the respective Gödel numbers of B, P, Q; let s, c, a be respective Gödel numbers of the symbols $*$, $,$, $\longrightarrow$, and for any number n, let $\bar{n}$ be the Gödel number of the numeral n. Let $v_1, \ldots, v_m$ be the Gödel number of the variables $x_1, \ldots, x_m$. Then $\varphi(i_1, \ldots, i_n) = bp\bar{i}_1c\bar{i}_2c\ldots c\bar{i}_ncv_1c\ldots cv_maqv_1c\ldots cv_msq$. [We use juxtaposition to denote concatenation to the base 2.]

N.B. It is obvious that the function $\varphi(z_1, \ldots, z_n)$ constructed in the above proof has the property that for all $i_1, \ldots, i_n$, $\varphi(i_1, \ldots, i_n)$ is greater than each of the numbers $i_1, \ldots, i_n$. We shall call a function having this property a <u>progressing</u> function.

Our next theorem is closer to Kleene's S^m_n theorem.

THEOREM 2.1. For every m, n: There is a recursive function (in fact a progressing recursive function) $\varphi(z, z_1, \ldots, z_n)$ such that for all numbers $e, i_1, \ldots, i_n$, if e is an index of an r.e. relation $M(z_1, \ldots, z_n, x, \ldots, x_m)$, $\varphi(e, i_1, \ldots, i_n)$ is an index of $M_{i_1,\ldots,i_n}$.

PROOF. By application of Theorem 2 to the universal relation $U(z, z_1, \ldots, z_n, x_1, \ldots, x_m)$.

---

[2] The function φ which we construct is actually primitive recursive (as in Kleene).

THEOREM 2.2. Let $\Psi_1^n, \Psi_2^n, \ldots, \Psi_i^n, \ldots$ be <u>any</u> enumeration of all r.e. relations of degree n such that the relation $M(z, x_1, \ldots, x_n)$, viz. $\Psi_z^n(x_1, \ldots, x_n)$, is r.e. Then there is a recursive function $\varphi(x)$ (in fact one which is progressing) such that for every i, $\Psi_i^n = R_{\varphi(i)}^n$.

PROOF. By Theorem 2 there is a (progressing) recursive function $\varphi(z)$ such that for all i, $\varphi(i)$ is an index of M_i. But $M_i = \Psi_i^n$, so $\varphi(i)$ is an index of Ψ_i^n — i.e., $R_{\phi(i)}^n = \Psi_i^n$.

REMARKS. Theorem 2.2 means that our method of indexing all r.e. attributes is such that for any other recursively enumerable enumeration, we can always effectively pass from an index of an r.e. attribute in the other enumeration to an index of the same attribute in our enumeration.

Our iteration theorem was of course stated relative to a particular indexing. The upshot of our preceeding remarks is that if an indexing is such that the iteration theorem holds, then it automatically has the above property. The converse is also easily verified. By taking $\Psi_i^n = R_i^n$, we immediately have the following theorem, due to Myhill and Dekker.

THEOREM 2.3. Given any index i of an r.e. attribute, we can effectively find a larger index of the same attribute. Stated otherwise: For each n there is a progressing recursive function $\varphi(x)$ such that for all i, $R_i^n = R_{\varphi(i)}^n$.

The next theorem is also due to Myhill and Dekker.

THEOREM 2.4. Given any index i of an r.e. attribute R_i, and any number m, we can effectively find a number $h(i, m)$ which both exceeds m and is an index of R_i.

PROOF. (Informal). We use the function $\varphi(x)$ of Theorem 2.3, and consider the sequence $i, \varphi(i), \varphi\varphi(i), \ldots$. We define $h(i, m)$ as the first element of this sequence which exceeds m.

Our next theorem generalizes, somewhat, a theorem of Myhill (Theorem 15, [14]). It will have another crucial application in Chapter V.

For $n = 1$, Theorem 2 says that for every r.e. relation $M(z, x_1, \ldots, x_m)$ there is a recursive function $t(z)$ such that for every i, $t(i)$ is an index of the relation $M(i, x_1, \ldots, x_2)$ — i.e., of $\lambda x, \ldots, x_n M(i, x_1, \ldots, x_n)$. Our next theorem says that this can be done with a $1 - 1$ recursive function $t(z)$.

THEOREM 2.5. For any r.e. relation $M(z, x_1, \ldots, x_n)$ there is a $1 - 1$ recursive function $t(z)$ (in fact one which is monotone strictly increasing) such that for all i, $t(i)$ is an index of the relation $M(i, x_1, \ldots, x_n)$. [i.e., for all $x_1, \ldots, x_n$, $R_{(t(i)}(x_1, \ldots, x_n) \longleftrightarrow M_i(x_1, \ldots, x_n)$.]

PROOF. (Informal). By Theorem 2 there is a recursive function $\varphi(z)$ such that for all i, $\varphi(i)$ is an index of M_i [i.e., of $\lambda x_1, \ldots, x_n M(i, x_1, \ldots, x_n)$]. We let $h(i, m)$ be the function of Theorem 2.4. We define $t(n)$ by mathematical induction, in the following manner:

$$t(1) = \varphi(1)$$
$$t(n+1) = h(\varphi(n+1), t(n)) \quad .$$

It is easy to verify that $t(x)$ is recursive. Clearly $t(n+1) > t(n)$, so $t(x)$ is monotone strictly increasing; hence $t(x)$ is $1-1$. And by definition of h, $R_{t(n+1)} = R_{\varphi(n+1)} = M_{n+1}$. And of course $R_{t(1)} = R_{\varphi(1)} = M(1, x_1, \ldots, x_n)$. So for all n, $R_{t(n)} = M_n$.

§4. EFFECTIVE OPERATIONS

For any number d we let Σ_d be the collection of all r.e. attributes of degree d. By $\Sigma_{d_1} \times \cdots \times \Sigma_{d_n}$ we mean the collection of all n-tuples $(A_1, \ldots, A_n)$ where A_1 is a r.e. attribute of degree $d_1, \ldots, A_n$ is a r.e. attribute of degree d_n. Consider now the numbers $d_1, \ldots, d_n, d$ and a mapping Φ from $\Sigma_{d_1} \times \cdots \times \Sigma_{d_n}$, (or a subset of $\Sigma_{d_1} \times \cdots \times \Sigma_{d_n}$) into Σ_d. We shall call Φ an <u>operation</u>. For any numerical function $\varphi(x_1, \ldots, x_n)$, we shall say that φ <u>mirrors</u> the the operation Φ iff for all $i_1, \ldots, i_n$ such that $(R_{i_1}, \ldots, R_{i_n})$ is in the domain of Φ, $\varphi(i_1, \ldots, i_n)$ is an index of $\Phi(R_{i_1}, \ldots, R_{i_n})$. [$R_{i_j}$ is the r.e. attribute of degree d_j whose index is i_j.] Stated otherwise: φ mirrors Φ iff whenever $i_1, \ldots, i_n$ are respective indices of $A_1, \ldots, A_n$ and $\Phi(A_1, \ldots, A_n)$ is defined, then $\varphi(i_1, \ldots, i_n)$ is an index of $\Phi(A_1, \ldots, A_n)$.

We now define Φ to be an <u>effective operation</u> iff it can be mirrored by a recursive function.[1] We shall often use the phrase "given any indices $i_1, \ldots, i_n$ of $A_1, \ldots, A_n$ we can effectively find an index $\varphi(i_1, \ldots, i_n$ of $\Phi(A_1, \ldots, A_n)$" to mean: "Φ is an effective operation; let φ be a recursive function which mirrors it".

We now consider the "effective" analogue of Theorem I – Chapter II.

THEOREM 3. The following operations are effective:

(1) Union.

(2) Intersection.

(3) All Explicit Transformations.

(4) Existential Quantification.

(5) Finite Quantification (both existential and universal).

We first prove:

---

[1] This notion of an effective operation is that of Myhill, Shepherdson [15].

LEMMA. If $M(z_1, \ldots, z_n, x_1, \ldots, x_n)$ is a r.e. relation such that for all $i_1, \ldots, i_n$ for which $\Phi(R_{i_1}, \ldots, R_{i_n})$ is defined, $M_{i_1}, \ldots, i_n = \Phi(R_{i_1}, \ldots, R_{i_n})$ [i.e., for all $x_1, \ldots, x_m$, $M(i_1, \ldots, i_n, x_1, \ldots, x_m) \longleftrightarrow (x_1, \ldots, x_m) \in \Phi(R_{i_1}, \ldots, R_{i_n})$] then Φ is an effective operation.

PROOF. By Theorem 2, there is a recursive function $\varphi(z_1, \ldots, z_n)$ such that $\varphi(i_1, \ldots, i_n)$ is an index of $M_{i_1,\ldots i_n}$. Hence if $\Phi(R_{i_1}, \ldots, R_{i_n})$ is defined, it has $\varphi(i_1, \ldots, i_n)$ as an index. Hence φ mirrors Φ.

PROOF OF THEOREM.

(1) Let Φ be the operation: $\Phi(R_i^n, R_j^n) = R_i^n \cup R_j^n$. Let $M(z_1, z_2, x_1, \ldots, x_n)$ be the r.e. relation:

$$U(z_1, x_1, \ldots, x_n) \vee U(z_2, x_1, \ldots, x_n) .$$

Then
$$\begin{aligned} M(i_1, i_2, x_1, \ldots, x_m) &\longleftrightarrow U(i_1, x_1, \ldots, x_n) \vee U(i_2, x_1, \ldots, x_n) \\ &\longleftrightarrow R_{i_1}^n (x_1, \ldots, x_n) \vee R_{i_2}^n (x_1, \ldots, x_n) \\ &\longleftrightarrow (x_1, \ldots, x_n) \in R_{i_1}^n \cup R_{i_2}^n \\ &\longleftrightarrow (x_1, \ldots, x_n) \in \Phi(R_{i_1}^n, R_{i_2}^n) . \end{aligned}$$

Thus $M_{i_1,i_2} = \Phi(R_{i_1}^n, R_{i_1}^n)$.

Then apply the preceding lemma.

(2) Analogous proof with $M(z_1, z_2, x_1, \ldots, x_n)$ the relation:

$$U(z_1, x_1, \ldots, x_n) \wedge U(z_2, x_1, \ldots, x_n) .$$

(3) Consider an explicit transformation $\Phi_{(x_1,\ldots,x_n;\xi,\ldots,\xi_k)}$ — i.e., the operation Φ which takes any r.e. relation R of degree k to the relation $\lambda x_1, \ldots, x_n R(\xi_1, \ldots, \xi_k)$.

Define $M(z, x_1, \ldots, x_n) \longleftrightarrow U(z, \xi_1, \ldots, \xi_k)$.

Then
$$\begin{aligned} M(i, x_1, \ldots, x_n) &\longleftrightarrow U(i, \xi_1, \ldots, \xi_k) \\ &\longleftrightarrow R_i(\xi_1, \ldots, \xi_k) \end{aligned}$$

So $M_i = (\lambda x_1, \ldots, x_n)R_i(\xi_1, \ldots, \xi_k) = \Phi(R_i)$.

Again apply the preceding lemma.

(4) Analogous proof, taking $M(z, x_1, \ldots, x_n)$ to be the r.e. relation: $(Ey)U(z, x_1, \ldots, x_n, y)$.

(5) For E_F, take

$$M(z, x_1, \ldots, x_n, w) \underset{df}{=} (Ey)_{<w} U(z, x_1, \ldots, x_n, y) .$$

For A_F take

$$M(z, x_1, \ldots, x_n, w) \underset{df}{=} (Ay)_{<w} U(z, x_1, \ldots, x_n, y) .$$

Since composition of recursive functions is recursive, it follows from Theorem 3 that any operation expressible as an iteration of any of the operations (1) - (5) is effective. For example, for any recursive function $f(x)$, given any index i of an attribute A we can effectively find an index $\varphi(i)$ of $f(A)$ [likewise an index $\Psi(i)$ of $f^{-1}(A)$]. Also there is a recursive function $\varphi(z_1, z_2)$ such that whenever i_1 is an index of a relation $f(x) = y$ and i_2 is an index of a r.e. attribute A, $\varphi(i_1, i_2)$ is an index of $f(A)$ [similarly with $f^{-1}(A)$]. Likewise the diagonal of a function $f(x, y)$ can be effectively found from $f(x, y)$ — i.e., given any index i of a recursive function $f(x, y)$ we can effectively find an index $\varphi(i)$ of $\vec{f}$.

§5. FIXED POINT THEOREMS

Our results in Chapter V will lean heavily on the fixed point theorems of this section. Myhill's fixed point theorem (cf. [14]) can be obtained as a consequence of the Kleene recursion theorem [12]. The latter can likewise be obtained as a consequence of the former, though the proof in this direction is more elaborate. We now consider a fixed point theorem from which both Myhill's theorem and Kleene's theorem will be derived.

THEOREM 4. For any r.e. relation $M(z, x_1, \ldots, x_n, y)$ there is a recursive function $t(x)$ such that for all numbers $i, x_1, \ldots, x_n$ we have:

$$R_{t(i)}(x_1, \ldots, x_n) \longleftrightarrow M(i, x_1, \ldots, x_n, t(i)) .$$

PROOF. By applying the iteration theorem to the r.e. relation $R_z(x_1, \ldots, x_n, z)$, we have a recursive function $d(z)$ such that for all $i, x_1, \ldots, x_n$:

(1) $$R_{d(i)}(x_1, \ldots, x_n) \longleftrightarrow R_i(x_1, \ldots, x_n, i) .$$

By applying the iteration theorem to the r.e. relation $M(z, x_1, \ldots, x_n, d(y))$ we have a recursive function $\varphi(z)$ such that for all $i, x_1, \ldots, x_n, y$:

(2) $$R_{\varphi(i)}(x_1, \ldots, x_n, y) \longleftrightarrow M(i, x_1, \ldots, x_n, d(y)) .$$

Then by (1), substituting $\varphi(i)$ for i, we have:

$$R_{d\varphi(i)}(x_1, \ldots, x_n) \longleftrightarrow R_{\varphi(i)}(x_1, \ldots, x_n, \varphi(i))$$

$$\longleftrightarrow M(i, x_1, \ldots, x_n, d\varphi(i))$$

[By (2), substituting $\varphi(i)$ for y].

Hence $R_{t(i)}(x_1, \ldots, x_n) \longleftrightarrow M(i, x_1, \ldots, x_n, t(i))$, where $t(i) \underset{df}{=} d\varphi(i)$.

REMARK. By using Theorem 2.5. in place of Theorem 2, the functions d and φ can both be chosen to be monotone strictly increasing, in which case t is then monotone strictly increasing. Hence Theorem 4 holds replacing "recursive" by "1 - 1 recursive". This is a crucial point in the proof of Myhill's theorem that any two creative sets are isomorphic. An analogous situation will arise when we come to Theorem 5.

THEOREM 4.1. For each n: There is a recursive function $t(z)$ such that for all $i, x_1, .., x_n$:

$$R_{t(i)}(x_1, \ldots, x_n) \longleftrightarrow R_i(x_1, \ldots, x_n, t(i)) \quad .$$

PROOF. By Theorem 4, taking $M(z, x_1, \ldots, x_n, y)$ to be the r.e. relation $R_z(x_1, \ldots, x_n, y)$.

REMARK. For $n = 1$, Theorem 4.1 reads: There is a recursive function $t(z)$ such that for all i, x,

$$x \in \omega_{t(i)} \longleftrightarrow R_i(x, t(i)) \quad .$$

This is Myhill's Fixed Point Theorem. We shall later show that Theorem 4.1 also yields Kleene's recursion theorem.

THEOREM 4.2. For any r.e. relation $M(z, x, y)$ there is a recursive function $t(z)$ such that for all i, x:

$$x \in \omega_{t(i)} \longleftrightarrow M(i, x, t(i)) \quad .$$

PROOF. This is a special case of Theorem 4, in which $n = 1$.

THEOREM 4.3. For any r.e. set α and r.e. relation $R(x, y)$ there is a recursive function $t(x)$ such that for every i and x:

$$x \in \omega_{t(i)} \longleftrightarrow i \in \alpha \wedge R(x, t(i)) \quad .$$

PROOF. By Theorem 4.2 taking $M(z, x, y)$ to be the r.e. relation $z \in \alpha \wedge R(x, y)$.

REMARK. The conclusion of Theorem 4.3 means that if $i \in \alpha$, $t(i)$ is an index of the set of all x such that $R(x, t(i))$; if $i \notin \alpha$, $t(i)$ is an index of the empty set.

THEOREM 4.4. For any r.e. set α and recursive function $g(x)$ there is a recursive function $t(x)$ such that for all i:

$$\text{(i)} \quad i \in \alpha \longrightarrow \omega_{t(i)} = \text{unit set } \{gt(i)\}$$

$$\text{(ii)} \quad i \notin \alpha \longrightarrow \omega_{t(i)} = \text{empty set } \emptyset .$$

PROOF. By Theorem 4.3, taking $R(x, y)$ to be the r.e. relation: $x = g(y)$.

The above theorem is the basis of Myhill's proof that every r.e. set is reducible to a creative set (cf. Chapter V). We will wish to establish some stronger results (in Chapter V) on "uniformly creative" collections of sets, and for this purpose we shall need some further consequences of Theorem 4.

In what follows, $J(x, y)$, $K(x)$, $L(x)$ are recursive functions having the properties: $KJ(x, y) = x$; $LJ(x, y) = y$. Also J is to be $1 - 1$. These functions can be the standard pairing functions; other examples will be given in #B of this chapter.

THEOREM 4.5. For any r.e. relation $M(z_1, z_2, x, y)$ there is a recursive function $t(x, y)$ such that for all i, j, x:

$$x \in \omega_{t(i,j)} \longleftrightarrow M(i, j, x, t(i, j)) .$$

PROOF. Let $M'(z, x, y)$ be the r.e. relation $M(Kz, Lz, x, y)$ (it is trivial to verify that this relation is r.e.). By Theorem 4.2 there is a recursive function $\varphi(x)$ such that for all i, x:

$$x \in \omega_{\varphi(i)} \longleftrightarrow M'(i, x, \varphi(i)) .$$

Substituting $J(i, j)$ for i we have:

$$\begin{aligned} x \in \omega_{\varphi J(i,j)} &\longleftrightarrow M'(J(i, j), x, \varphi J(i, j)) \\ &\longleftrightarrow M(KJ(i, j), LJ(i, j), x, \varphi J(i, j)) \\ &\longleftrightarrow M(i, j, x, \varphi J(i, j)) . \end{aligned}$$

So the recursive function $t(i, j)$; viz. $\varphi J(i, j)$, has the desired property.

THEOREM 4.6. For any r.e. set α and recursive function $g(x, y)$ there is a recursive function $t(x, y)$ such that for every i, j, x the following holds:

(1) $j \in \alpha \longrightarrow t_1(j)$ index of $\{g_1 t_1(j)\}$.

(2) $j \notin \alpha \longrightarrow t_1(j)$ index of $\emptyset$.

$[t_1(x) \underset{df}{=} t(i, x);\ g_1(x) \underset{df}{=} g(i, x)]$.

PROOF. Let $M(z_1, z_2, x, y)$ be the r.e. relation:

$z_2 \in \alpha \wedge x = g(z_1, y)$ — written otherwise:

$z_2 \in \alpha \wedge x = g_{z_1}(y)$.

By Theorem 4.5, there is a recursive function $t(x, y)$ such that:

$$x \in \omega_{t_1(j)} \longleftrightarrow M(i, j, x, t_1(j))$$

$$\longleftrightarrow j \in \alpha \wedge x = g_1 t_1(j) \ .$$

Thus $\omega_{t_1(j)} = \{x : j \in \alpha \wedge x = g_1 t_1(j)\}$

[i.e., $= \lambda x(j \in \alpha \wedge x = g_1 t_1(j))$] .

For $j \in \alpha$, $\{x : j \in \alpha \wedge x = g_1 t_1(j)\}$ = unit set $\{g_1 t_1(j)\}$.

For $j \notin \alpha$, $\{x : j \in \alpha \wedge x = g_1 t_1(j)\} = \emptyset$.

It is Theorem 4.6 rather than Theorem 4.5 which will have direct subsequent applications.

§6. DOUBLE RECURSION THEOREMS

A Double Analogue of Theorem 4. For our main investigations in Chapter V (concerning effective inseparability) the following "double analogues" of Theorem 4 (and some of its consequences) will be crucial.

THEOREM 5. For any two r.e. relations $M_1(z, x_1, \ldots, x_n, y)$ and $M_2(z, x_1, \ldots, x_n, y)$ a $1 - 1$ recursive function $t(z)$ can be found such that for all numbers $i, x_1, \ldots, x_n$ the following conditions simultaneously hold:

(1) $R_{Kt(i)}(x_1, \ldots, x_n) \longleftrightarrow M_1(i, x_1, \ldots, x_n, t(i))$

(2) $R_{Lt(i)}(x_1, \ldots, x_n) \longleftrightarrow M_2(i, x_1, \ldots, x_n, t(i))$.

PROOF. We illustrate the proof for $n = 1$. [This is the only case which we shall actually use. The proof for arbitrary n can be obtained by just substituting "$x_1, \ldots, x_n$" for "x".]

The conditions (relations) $R_{Kz}(x, z)$ and $R_{Lz}(x, z)$ are easily shown to be r.e. Then by Theorem 2.5 there are $1 - 1$ recursive functions $d_1(z)$, $d_2(z)$ such that for all numbers i, x:

$$x \in \omega_{d_1(i)} \longleftrightarrow R_{K(i)}(x, i)$$

$$x \in \omega_{d_2(i)} \longleftrightarrow R_{L(i)}(x, i) \quad .$$

Let $d(z) = J(d_1(z), d_2(z))$. Then $d(z)$ is a $1 - 1$ recursive function such that for all z, $Kd(z) = d_1(z)$ and $Ld(z) = d_2(z)$. Hence

(1)
$$x \in \omega_{Kd(i)} \longleftrightarrow R_{K(i)}(x, i)$$

$$x \in \omega_{Ld(i)} \longleftrightarrow R_{L(i)}(x, i)$$

Also, the relations $M_1(z, x, d(y))$ and $M_2(z, x, d(y))$ are r.e., so there are $1 - 1$ recursive functions $\varphi_1(x)$, $\varphi_2(x)$ such that for all i, x, y:

$$R_{\varphi_1(i)}(x, y) \longleftrightarrow M_1(i, x, d(y))$$

$$R_{\varphi_2(i)}(x, y) \longleftrightarrow M_2(i, x, d(y)) \quad .$$

Let $\varphi(z) = J[\varphi_1(z), \varphi_2(z)]$. Then $\varphi(z)$ is a $1 - 1$ recursive function such that for all z, $K\varphi(z) = \varphi_1(z)$ and $L\varphi(z) = d_2(z)$.

Then for all i and x:

(2)
$$R_{K\varphi(i)}(x, y) \longleftrightarrow M_1(i, x, d(y))$$

$$R_{L\varphi(i)}(x, y) \longleftrightarrow M_2(i, x, d(y)) \quad .$$

By (2) we have (substituting "$\varphi(i)$" for "y")

(3)
$$R_{K\varphi(i)}(x, \varphi(i) \longleftrightarrow M_1(i, x, d\varphi(i))$$

$$R_{L\varphi(i)}(x, \varphi(i) \longleftrightarrow M_2(i, x, d\varphi(i)) \quad .$$

By (1) we have (substituting "$\varphi(i)$" for "i")

(4)
$$x \in \omega_{Kd\varphi(i)} \longleftrightarrow R_{K\varphi(i)}(x, \varphi(i))$$

$$x \in \omega_{Ld\varphi(i)} \longleftrightarrow R_{L\varphi(i)}(x, \varphi(i))$$

But the right sides of the equivalences of (4) are the left sides of the equivalences of (3).

$$\therefore \quad x \in \omega_{Kd\varphi(i)} \longleftrightarrow M_1(i, x, d\varphi i)$$

$$x \in \omega_{Ld\varphi(i)} \longleftrightarrow M_2(i, x, d\varphi i) \quad .$$

So take $t(z) = d\varphi(z)$ and we have:

$$x \in \omega_{Kt(i)} \longleftrightarrow M_1(i, x, t(i))$$

$$x \in \omega_{Lt(i)} \longleftrightarrow M_2(i, x, t(i)) \quad .$$

Also, t is $1 - 1$, since d and φ are $1 - 1$. This concludes the proof.[1]

THEOREM 5.1. Let α, β be two r.e. sets; let $f(x)$, $g(x)$ be two recursive functions. Then there is a $1 - 1$ recursive function $t(x)$ such that for every number i:

$i \in \alpha \longrightarrow Kt(i)$ index of unit set $\{ft(i)\}$.
$i \notin \alpha \longrightarrow Kt(i)$ index of empty set.
$i \in \beta \longrightarrow Lt(i)$ index of $\{gt(i)\}$.
$i \notin \beta \longrightarrow Lt(i)$ index of empty set.

Thus if α and β are disjoint then

(1) $i \in \alpha \longrightarrow \{\omega_{Kt(i)}, \omega_{Lt(i)}\} = \{\{f(t(i))\}, \emptyset\}$.

(2) $i \in \beta \longrightarrow \{\omega_{Kt(i)}, \omega_{Lt(i)}\} = \{\emptyset, \{gt(i)\}\}$.

(3) $i \notin \alpha \cup \beta \longrightarrow \{\omega_{Kt(i)}, \omega_{Lt(i)}\} = \{\emptyset, \emptyset\}$.

PROOF. Take $M_1(z, x, y)$ to be the relation: $z \in \alpha \wedge x = f(y)$
Take $M_2(z, x, y)$ to be the relation: $z \in \beta \wedge x = g(y)$.

Then apply Theorem 5.

Actually, we shall only need the above theorem for the special case: $g(x) = f(x)$.

#B. CONSTRUCTIVE ARITHMETIC AND RUDIMENTARY ATTRIBUTES

In this section we introduce a sub-class of the constructive arithmetic attributes which we call <u>rudimentary</u> attributes. We first show that all rudimentary attributes are indeed constructive arithmetic, then we show that the rudimentary attributes form a basis for the r.e. attributes (and hence that the constructive arithmetic attributes form a basis).

[1] This proof, like that of Theorem 4, appeals to the iteration theorem. Hilary Putnam has subsequently shown (oral communication) that Theorem 5 can be obtained as a direct consequence of Theorem 4.

As remarked in the Preface, our proof follows novel lines in that all appeal to the traditional number theory devices accorded this in the past — e.g., prime factorization, congruences and the Chinese remainder theorem — are avoided. Thus Gödel's program of establishing incompleteness, even of first order theories involving plus and times as their sole arithmetical primitives, can, by the methods of this section, be carried out without appeal to number theory.

§7. SOME PRELIMINARIES

PROPOSITION 1. (a) For any attribute $R(x_1, \ldots, x_n, y)$ the following attributes are constructively definable from R:

(1) $(Ey)_{\leq z} R(x_1, \ldots, x_n, y)$

(2) $(Ay)_{\leq z} R(x_1, \ldots, x_n, y)$.

(b) For any attribute $R(x_1, \ldots, x_n, x, y)$ the following attributes are constructively definable from R:

(3) $(Ey)_{<x} R(x_1, \ldots, x_n, x, y)$
i.e., $\lambda x_1, \ldots, x_n, x\ (Ey)_{<x} R(x_1, \ldots, x_n, x, y)$

(4) $(Ey)_{\leq x} R(x_1, \ldots, x_n, x, y)$

(5) $(Ay)_{<x} R(x_1, \ldots, x_n, x, y)$

(6) $(Ay)_{\leq x} R(x_1, \ldots, x_n, x, y)$.

PROOF. Let the relations defined in (1) - (6) respectively be $R_1, \ldots, R_6$. Then:

(1) $R_1(x_1,\ldots,x_n,z) \longleftrightarrow (Ey)_{<z} R(x_1, \ldots, x_n, y) \vee R(x_1, \ldots, x_n, z)$ — this proves (1).

(2) $R_2(x_1,\ldots,x_n,z) \longleftrightarrow (Ay)_{<z} R(x_1, \ldots, x_n, y) \wedge R(x_1, \ldots, x_n, z)$ — this proves (2).

(3) Let $S(x_1, \ldots, x_n, x, z)$ be the relation: $(Ey)_{<z} R(x_1, \ldots, x_n, x, y)$. S is constructively definable from R. Also $R_3(x_1, \ldots, x_n, x) \longleftrightarrow S(x_1, \ldots, x_n, x, x)$, so R_3 is explicitly definable from S. Hence R_3 is constructively definable from R. This proves (3).

(4), (5), (6) are proved analogously.

It is obvious that if A is constructively definable from $A_1, \ldots, A_n$ and if each A_i is constructively definable from $B_1, \ldots, B_m$ then A is constructively definable from $B_1, \ldots, B_m$. Thus, e.g., if R is constructive arithmetic then each of the attributes $R_1, \ldots, R_6$ of Proposition 1 is constructive arithmetic.

PROPOSITION 2. (a) The relations $x = y$, $x < y$, $x \leq y$ are constructive arithmetic.

(b) The relation x divides y (abbreviated x div y) is constructive arithmetic.

PROOF. (a) $x = y \longleftrightarrow x \times 1 = y$

$$x < y \longleftrightarrow (Ez)_{<y}\ [x + z = y]\ .$$

$$x \leq y \longleftrightarrow x < y \vee x = y$$

(b) $x \text{ div } y \longleftrightarrow (x = 1) \vee (Ez)_{<y}\ (x \times z = y)\ .$

PROPOSITION 3. If n is a prime number then the set Ω_n of all powers of n is constructive arithmetic.[1] In particular, Ω_2 is constructive arithmetic.

PROOF. Let n be prime. Then x is a power of n iff every divisor of x is divisible by n. Hence (for n a prime) we have:

$$x \in \Omega_n \longleftrightarrow (Ay)_{\leq x}\ [(y \text{ div } x \wedge (1 < y)) \longrightarrow n \text{ div } y]\ .^{2}$$

§8. DYADIC CONCATENATION

For any number x we let $\bar{x}$ be the dyadic numeral which designates x (in dyadic notation). Until further notice we shall feel free to identify numbers with their corresponding dyadic numerals. For any numbers x, y by xy, or x * y, we shall mean that number z such that $\bar{x}\bar{y}$ (i.e., $\bar{x}$ followed by $\bar{y}$) = $\bar{z}$ — e.g., 121 * 22 = 12122. We let C(x, y, z) be the relation $\bar{x}\bar{y} = \bar{z}$, and we wish to prove that C is constructive arithmetic.

We note that $x * y = [x \times 2^{l(y)}] + y$, where $l(y)$ is the <u>length</u> of the numeral $\bar{y}$. We obviously need:

LEMMA. The relation $y = 2^{l(x)}$ is constructive arithmetic.

PROOF. We first note the following relationships. For any number r, the smallest number of length r is

$$\underbrace{11 \ldots 1}_{r} = 2^r - 1\ .$$

---

[1] For this proposition, which is crucial in our subsequent developments, the author is indebted to John Myhill.

[2] Our use of the implication symbol fits into the scheme of constructive definability, since $p \longrightarrow q$ iff $\sim p \vee q$.

The largest number of length r is

$$\underbrace{22\ldots2}_{r} \quad .$$

Thus a number x has length r iff x lies between $2^r - 1$ and $2(2^r - 1)$ — i.e., $l(x) = r \longleftrightarrow (2^r - 1) \leq x \leq 2(2^r - 1)$. (1)

We next note that $y = 2^{l(x)}$ iff the two following conditions hold:

$C_1 : \Omega_2(y)$ — i.e., y is a power of 2.

$C_2 : y - 1 \leq x \leq 2(y - 1)$.

For suppose $y = 2^{l(x)}$. Let $r = l(x)$. Then $y = 2^r$, hence by (1), $y - 1 \leq x \leq 2(y - 1)$ — i.e., (C_2) holds. And of course (C_1) holds.

Conversely, suppose C_1 and C_2 hold. Then by C_1, $y = 2^r$ for some r. And by C_2, $2^r - 1 \leq x \leq 2(2^r - 1)$, so $r = l(x)$, by (1). Thus $y = 2^{l(x)}$.

It remains only to verify that condition C_2 is constructive arithmetic. (Condition C_1 is by Proposition 3.) We must show that each of the conditions: $y - 1 \leq x$; $x \leq 2(y - 1)$ are constructive arithmetic.

(a) $y - 1 \leq x \longleftrightarrow y \leq x + 1$

$\longleftrightarrow (Ez)_{\leq x}(y = z + 1)$. Thus the first condition is constructive arithmetic.

(b) $x \leq 2(y - 1) \longleftrightarrow x \leq (y - 1) + (y - 1)$

$$\longleftrightarrow (Ev, w)_{<y}\ [v + w = x] \ .$$

Thus the second condition is also constructive arithmetic.

Now we have:

THEOREM. The relation $x * y = z$ is constructive arithmetic.

PROOF. $x * y = z \longleftrightarrow (x \times 2^{l(y)}) + y = z$

$$\longleftrightarrow (Ev, w)_{<z}\ [v = 2^{l(y)} \wedge x \times v = w \wedge w + y = z] \ .$$

The relation $v = 2^{l(y)}$ is constructive arithmetic by the preceding lemma.

§9. RUDIMENTARY ATTRIBUTES

We now define a rudimentary attribute as one which is constructively definable from the dyadic concatenation relation $C(x, y, z)$. Since C is constructive arithmetic, we immediately have:

THEOREM 6. All rudimentary attributes are constructive arithmetic.

We do not know whether or not all constructive arithmetic attributes are rudimentary. Quine [19] has shown that plus and times are first order definable from C — in fact it is easy to show that plus and times are each of the form $(Ey)R(x_1, x_2, x_3, y)$, where R is rudimentary, but this leaves unanswered the question as to whether plus and times are themselves rudimentary.[1] At any rate, the remainder of #B will be devoted to showing that various key attributes in recursive function theory are in fact rudimentary (a-fortiori, constructive arithmetic).[2]

The techniques we now employ are constructive analogues and extensions of those of Quine [19]. We say that x is part of y (abbreviated "xPy") iff the dyadic numeral $\bar{x}$ is part of the dyadic numeral $\bar{y}$. We analogously define the relations "x begins y" abbreviated "xBy" and "x ends y" abbreviated "xEy". We say that x is a tally (abbreviated "$\sigma(x)$") iff x is a string of 1's. [These terms are all Quine's [19].]

PROPOSITION 4. The following attributes are rudimentary.

(a) $x = y$

(b) [For each n] $x_1 * \cdots * x_n = y$

(c) xBy, xEy, xPy

(d) $x_1 * \cdots * x_nBy$, $x_1 * \cdots * x_nEy$, $x_1 * \cdots * x_nPy$

(e) σx

(f) $x < y$, $x \leq y$.

PROOF.

(a) $x = y \Longleftrightarrow (Ez_1, z_2)_{<x} [z_1 * z_2 = x \wedge z_1 * z_2 = y] \vee$

$$[x * 1 = 11 \wedge y * 1 = 11] \vee [x * 1 = 21 \wedge y * 1 = 21].$$

(b) $x_1 * \cdots * x_n = y \Longleftrightarrow (Ey_3, \ldots, y_{n-1})_{<y}$

$$[x_1x_2 = y_3 \wedge y_3x_4 = y_4 \wedge \cdots \wedge y_{n-1}x_n = y].$$

---

[1] The case for plus has been recently answered affirmatively by Robert Ritchie (oral communication).

[2] All rudimentary attributes are, of course, primitive recursive, but not conversely. Ritchie has recently shown (oral communication) that the rudimentary attributes (in fact the constructive arithmetic attributes) constitute a sub-class of the relations associated with Gregorzyk's class ε_o (cf. [9]).

(c) $xBy \longleftrightarrow x = y \vee (Ez)_{<y}(xz = y)$.

$xEy \longleftrightarrow x = y \vee (Ez)_{<y}(zx = y)$.

$xPy \longleftrightarrow xBy \vee xEy \vee (Ez_1, z_2)_{<y}(z_1 x z_2 = y)$.

(d) $x_1 * \ldots * x_n By \longleftrightarrow (Ez)_{<y}\ [x_1 * \ldots * x_n = z \wedge zBy]$

[Analogously with "E" and "P"].

(e) $\sigma x \longleftrightarrow 2\tilde{P}x$

(f) $x < y \longleftrightarrow (Ez)_{<y}(z = x)$; $x \leq y \longleftrightarrow (Ez)_{\leq y}(z = x)$.

<u>Finite Sequences</u>. For any number π we let $\mathring{\pi} = 2\pi 2$.

Consider any finite sequence $(x_1, \ldots, x_n)$. Let $(x_1, \ldots, x_n)^{\#}$ be the number $\mathring{\pi}x_1\mathring{\pi}x_2\mathring{\pi}\ldots\mathring{\pi}x_n\mathring{\pi}$, where π is the smallest tally which is larger than any tally which occurs as part of any of the x_i. We call $(x_1, \ldots, x_n)^{\#}$ the <u>sequence number</u> of the sequence $(x_1, \ldots, x_n)$. It is obvious that for each $i \leq n$, $(x_1, \ldots, x_n)^{\#} > x_i$. It is also obvious that if $(x_1, \ldots, x_n)^{\#} = (y_1, \ldots, y_m)^{\#}$ then $n = m$ and $x_1 = y_1, \ldots, x_n = y_n$. We let Seq be the set of all sequence numbers. We let "$x \in y$" be the relation: y is a sequence number of some sequence of which x is a term. We let "$x \in_F y$" be the relation: x is the final element of (the sequence whose sequence number is) y. We let $x \underset{w}{<} y$ be the relation "x occurs earlier than y in the sequence whose sequence number is w" [this is to imply that w is a sequence number].

We wish to show that the conditions $Seq(x)$, $x \in y$, $x \in_F y$, $x \underset{w}{<} y$ are all rudimentary and that for each number n, the relation $(x_1, \ldots, x_n)^{\#} = y$ is rudimentary. We first abbreviate the expression "$\sigma v \wedge vPy \wedge v1\tilde{P}y$" by "$v\ell ty$" (read "$v$ is the longest tally in y"). We next consider the set Seq_1 of all numbers of the form $\mathring{v}x_1\mathring{v}\ldots\mathring{v}x_n\mathring{v}$, where v is a tally which is not part of any of the x_i. [Such a number is not necessarily a sequence number; it is a sequence number only if either $v = 1$ or else v is of the form $y1$, where y is part of at least one of the x_i.] The set Seq_1 is rudimentary, for $Seq_1(w) \longleftrightarrow (Ev)_{<w}[v\ell tw \wedge \mathring{v}Bw \wedge \mathring{v}Ew \wedge \mathring{v} \neq w \wedge \mathring{v}\mathring{v}\tilde{P}w \wedge 2v2v2\tilde{P}w]$. We also let $x \in_1 w$ be the rudimentary relation: $(Ev)_{<w}[v\ell tw \wedge \mathring{v}x\mathring{v}Pw \wedge v\tilde{P}x]$.

PROPOSITION 5. The following attributes are rudimentary:

(a) Seq w

(b) $x \in w$

(c) $x \in_F w$

(d) $x \underset{w}{<} y$

(e) [For each n] the relation $y = (x_1, \ldots, x_n)^{\#}$.

PROOF.

(a) $\text{Seq } w \longleftrightarrow \text{Seq}_1 w \wedge [1\ell tw \vee (Ex, y)_{<w} (x\epsilon_1 w \wedge y\ell x \wedge {}^2y1{}^2Bw]$.

(b) $x \in w \longleftrightarrow \text{Seq } w \wedge x \in_1 w$.

(c) $x \in_F w \longleftrightarrow x \in w \wedge (Ev)_{<w}[v\ell tw \wedge \mathring{v}x\mathring{v}Ew]$.

(d) $x \underset{w}{<} y \longleftrightarrow x \in w \wedge y \in w \wedge (Ev)_{<w}[v\ell tw \wedge (\mathring{v}x\mathring{v}y\mathring{v}Pw \vee$
$(Ez)_{<w}\mathring{v}x\mathring{v}z\mathring{v}y\mathring{v}Pw)]$.

(e) $y = (x_1, \ldots, x_n)^{\#} \longleftrightarrow \text{Seq } y \wedge (Ev)_{<y}$
$[v\ell ty \wedge y = \mathring{v}x_1\mathring{v}\ldots\mathring{v}x_n\mathring{v}]$.

<u>The function</u> θ. For any number x, if x is a sequence number $(x_1, \ldots, x_n)^{\#}$, we define $\theta(x) = x_n$; otherwise $\theta(x) = 1$.

We call a function $f(x_1, \ldots, x_n)$ rudimentary iff the relation $f(x_1, \ldots, x_n) = y$ is rudimentary.

PROPOSITION 6. The function θ is rudimentary.

PROOF. $\theta(x) = y \longleftrightarrow (\text{seq } x \wedge y \in_F x) \vee (\sim \text{Seq } x \wedge y = 1)$.

REMARK. We shall subsequently use the function θ to obtain a rudimentary analogue of the Kleene function $U(x)$. (cf. §11).

<u>Ordered Pairs</u>. We let $J(x, y) = (x, y)^{\#}$. For any number z, if z is of the form $J(x, y)$, define $K(z) = x$; $L(z) = y$. If z is not of the form $J(x, y)$, define $K(z) = 1$; $L(z) = 1$.

PROPOSITION 7. The functions K and L are rudimentary.

PROOF. The relation $K(x) = y$ is the disjunction of the following two rudimentary conditions:

(1) $(Ex_1, x_2)_{<x}[J(x_1, x_2) = x \wedge y = x_1]$.

(2) $(Ax_1, x_2)_{<x} [J(x_1, x_2) \neq x \wedge y = 1]$.

Proof for L is analogous.

PROGRESSING FUNCTIONS

PROPOSITION 8. If $f(x_1, \ldots, x_n)$ is rudimentary and progressing (cf. note following Theorem 2) and if $g_1, \ldots, g_m$ are rudimentary functions then $f[g_1(x_1, \ldots, x_n), \ldots, g_m(x_1, \ldots, x_n)]$ is rudimentary.

PROOF. $f[g_1(x_1, \ldots, x_n), \ldots, g_m(x_1, \ldots, x_n)] = y \longleftrightarrow$
$(Ez_1, \ldots, z_m)_{<y} [g_1(x_1, \ldots, x_n) = z_1 \wedge \ldots \wedge g_m(x_1, \ldots, x_n)$
$= z_m \wedge f(z_1, \ldots, z_m) = y]$.

It will be convenient to adopt the notations:

$J_3(x_1, x_2, x_3)$ for $J(x_1, J(x_2, x_3))$

$J_4(x_1, x_2, x_3, x_4)$ for $J(x_1, J_3(x_2, x_3, x_4))$

.
.
.

$J_n(x_1, \ldots, x_n)$ for $J(x_1, J_{n-1}(x_2, x_3, \ldots, x_n))$.

It is obvious by Proposition 8 that each of the functions J_3, J_4, ... are rudimentary (and also progressing).

*A Rudimentary β-function. Gödel [8] constructed the well known primitive recursive function $\beta(x, y, z)$ having the property that for any finite sequence $(x_1, \ldots, x_n)$ there exists numbers c, d such that for all $i \leq n$, $\beta(c, d, i) = x_i$. We now construct a rudimentary function $\beta(x, z)$ such that for any finite sequence $(x_1, \ldots, x_n)$ there is a number x such that for all $i \leq n$, $\beta(x, i) = x_i$.

We define $\beta(x, i)$ as that unique number j such that $J(i, j) \in x$ if there is such a unique number j; otherwise $\beta(x, i) \underset{df}{=} 1$.

It is clear that $\beta(x, y)$ has the desired properties, for let $(x_1, \ldots, x_n)$ be any finite sequence. Let $x = (J(1, x_1), \ldots, J(n, x_n))^{\#}$. Then it is obvious that for each $i \leq n$, $\beta(x, i) = x_i$.

PROPOSITION 9. The function $\beta(x, y)$ is rudimentary.

PROOF. Let $B(x, y, z)$ be the rudimentary relation:

$$J(y, z) \in x \wedge (Az')_{<x} [z' \neq z \longrightarrow J(y, z') \notin x] .$$

Then $\beta(x, y) = z \longleftrightarrow B(x, y, z) \vee [\sim (Ew)_{<x}(B(x, y, w) \wedge z = 1]$.

§10. PURE ELEMENTARY FORMAL SYSTEMS

Preparatory to the main task of this section; viz., the arithmetization of elementary formal systems, we shall consider a special type of elementary formal system which we term a pure system. These systems are adequate for the representation of all f.r. attributes, and their arithmetization is simpler than that of an arbitrary E.F.S. (cf. §11).

Let t be a term of an elementary formal system (E) over K. We shall call t a pure term iff t is either a variable or a single symbol of K. And we shall call F a pure formula iff all the terms which occur in it are pure. We shall call (E) a pure elementary formal system iff there exists a 3-place predicate which we will call "C" (which is to represent the "concatenation" relation) such that: (1) Cx,y,xy is an axiom of (E); (2) all other axioms of (E) are pure.

Now, given any attribute W which is f.r. over K, it is always possible to construct a pure E.F.S. (E)' over K in which W is represented. The general procedure is as follows: Let (E) be an E.F.S. over K in which P represents W. We first take a new 3-place predicate "C" and immediately put the formula Cx, y, xy as an axiom of (E)'. Now let A be any axiom of (E). If A is already pure, we take it as an axiom of (E)'. Otherwise, we apply the following "purification" process: If π_1, π_2 are each either a variable or a symbol of K and if $\pi_1\pi_2$ occurs as a constituent of some term of A, we take a new variable — call it "y" — and replace all occurrences of $\pi_1\pi_2$ in A by y and then add the expression Cπ_1, π_2, y as an additional premise. If the resulting formula A_1 is pure, we take it as an axiom of (E). Otherwise we repeat the "purification" process until A_1 is finally reduced to a pure formula A', which we then take as an axiom of (E)'. We do this in turn for each of the axioms of (E).

As an example, let W be the set of all words in {a, b, c} such that ab occurs as a constituent. It is represented by P in the following E.F.S. (E):

(1) Pab
(2) Pxab
(3) Pabx
(4) Pxaby

But W is also represented by P in the following pure system (E'):

(0) Cx, y, xy
(1)' Ca, b, x ⟶ Px
(2)' Cx, a, y ⟶ Cy, b, z ⟶ Pz
(3)' Ca, b, y ⟶ Cy, x, z ⟶ Pz
(4)' Cx, a, x_1 ⟶ Cx_1, b, x_2 ⟶ Cx_2, y, z ⟶ Pz .

The axioms (1)', ..., (4)' are respective purifications of the axioms (1), ..., (4) of (E).

§11. ARITHMETIZATION OF ELEMENTARY DYADIC ARITHMETICS

Let (E) be a <u>pure</u> E.F.S. over {1, 2}. By §10 all r.e. attributes are representable in such systems. We shall look at (E) as a collection of axiom <u>schemata</u> (cf. §2, Chapter I). By a sentence we mean (as in Chapter I) a w.f.f. of (E) which contains no variables.

We assign Gödel numbers to all <u>sentences</u> of (E) in the following manner. To each of the predicates of (E) we assign distinct numbers, which we call <u>predicate numbers</u>; this can be done in any manner providing no predicate number is of the form $J(x, y)$ [e.g., we can pick our predicate number from numbers in which 2 does not occur as a part]. Then to any atomic sentence $Pa_1, \ldots, a_n$ we assign the Gödel number $J(p, (a_1, \ldots, a_n)^{\#})$, where p is the predicate number of P. Then for any atomic sentences $F_1, \ldots, F_n$ with respective Gödel numbers $f_1, \ldots, f_n$, we let $J_n(f_1, \ldots, f_n)$ be the Gödel number of the compound sentence $F_1 \longrightarrow F_2 \longrightarrow \cdots \longrightarrow F_n$.

We note that every Gödel number of a sentence is uniquely of the form $J(a, b)$, where either a is a predicate number and b is a sequence number or a is the Gödel number of an atomic sentence A and b is the Gödel number of a sentence B (in which case $J(a, b)$ is the Gödel number of the sentence $A \longrightarrow B$). We also note that no predicate number can also be the Gödel number of a sentence (since a sentence number is of the form $J(x, y)$) — this was our reason for insisting that predicate numbers were not of the form $J(x, y)$. From this it follows that if a and $J(a, b)$ are both theorem numbers (i.e., Gödel numbers of provable sentences) then b is a theorem number (by the rule of detachment). In fact the set T_0 of theorem numbers is precisely the smallest set which includes the set A_0 of axiom numbers (Gödel numbers of axioms) and has the above closure property.

A_0 <u>is rudimentary</u>. For suppose we take any pure axiom scheme F of (E) — e.g., let $F = P_1x, 2 \longrightarrow P_2 1, y \longrightarrow P_3 x, y, 2$. Let $I(F)$ be the set of Gödel numbers of all instances of F. We assert that $I(F)$ is a rudimentary set. In the example just considered, a number z is in $I(F)$ iff there exist numbers x, y both less than z, such that $z = J_3[J(p_1, (x, 2)^{\#}), J(p_2, (1, y)^{\#}), J(p_3, (x, y, 2)^{\#})]$. [Since J_3, J are rudimentary progressing, then this condition is rudimentary.] More generally, let F be a pure formula $P_1 b_1^1, \ldots, b_{i_1}^1 \longrightarrow \cdots \longrightarrow P_r b_1^r, \ldots, b_{i_r}^r$, where each b_j^i is either a variable or one of the symbols "1", "2". Let $x_1, \ldots, x_n$ be the variables which occur amongst the b_j^i. Then the condition $x \in I(F)$ can be written down in the rudimentary form:

$$(Ex_1, \ldots, x_n)_{<x}[x = J_r[J(p_1, (b_1^1, \ldots, b_{i_1}^1)^{\#}), \ldots, J(p_r, (b_1^r, \ldots, b_{i_r}^r)^{\#})]].$$

So for any pure axiom schema F of (E), $I(F)$ is a rudimentary set. And for the one impure axiom schema Cx, y, xy of (E), the set S of Gödel numbers of its instances is rudimentary, for $x \in S \longleftrightarrow$

$$(Ex_1, x_2, x_3)_{<x}\ [x_1 x_2 = x_3 \wedge x = J(c, (x_1, x_2, x_3)^{\#})]$$

[c is the Gödel number of the predicate C].

Since there are but finitely many axiom schemata of (E), and for each such schema F, I(F) is rudimentary, we have:

LEMMA. The set A_o of axiom numbers of (E) is rudimentary.

PROOF SEQUENCES. By a <u>proof</u> in (E) we mean a finite sequence $X_1, \ldots, X_n$ of sentences of (E) such that each X_k is either an axiom of (E) or else is obtainable from earlier members X_i, X_j by the rule of detachment. If $X_1, \ldots, X_n$ have respective Gödel numbers $x_1, \ldots, x_n$ and if $X_1, \ldots, X_n$ is a proof, then we shall say that $(x_1, \ldots, x_n)$ is a <u>proof sequence</u> and that $(x_1, \ldots, x_n)^{\#}$ is a <u>proof number</u>. We let Pf be the set of all proof numbers and ypfx be the relation: y is a sequence number of some proof sequence whose last term is x — equivalently, $Pf(y) \wedge x \epsilon_F y$.

We note that $(x_1, \ldots, x_n)$ is a proof sequence iff each x_k of the sequence is either an axiom number or else there exist earlier x_i, x_j of the sequence such that $x_j = J(x_i, x_k)$. It is now easy to prove:

PROPOSITION 10. The following attributes are rudimentary:

(a) Pf w

(b) y pf x

(c) $y \text{ pf } J(x, (x_1, \ldots, x_n)^{\#})$. [That is, for each n the attribute $y \text{ pf } J(x, (x_1, \ldots, x_n)^{\#})$ is rudimentary.]

PROOF.

(a) $$\text{Pf } w \longleftrightarrow \text{Seq } w \wedge (Ax)_{<w}[x \in w \longrightarrow [A_o(x) \vee (Ex_1, x_2)_{<w} [x_1 \underset{w}{<} x \wedge x_2 \underset{w}{<} x \wedge x_2 = J(x_1, x)]]]$$

(b) $$y \text{ pf } x \longleftrightarrow \text{Pf } y \wedge x \epsilon_F y$$

(c) $$y \text{ pf } J(x, (x_1, \ldots, x_n)^{\#}) \longleftrightarrow (Ey_1, y_2)_{<y} [(x_1, \ldots, x_n)^{\#} = y_1 \wedge J(x, y_1) = y_2 \wedge y \text{ pf } y_2].$$

<u>Rudimentary Attributes as a Basis for r.e. Attributes</u>

Let us now take any attribute $R(x_1, \ldots, x_n)$ representable in (E); let P represent R and let p be its Gödel number. Then $(x_1, \ldots, x_n) \in R \longleftrightarrow Px_1, \ldots, x_n \in T \longleftrightarrow J(p, (x_1, \ldots, x_n)^{\#}) \in T_o \longleftrightarrow (Ey)(y \text{ pf } J(p, (x_1, \ldots, x_n)^{\#})$. Let $M(x_1, \ldots, x_n, y)$ be the relation $y \text{ pf } J(p, x_1, \ldots, x_n)^{\#})$. This relation is rudimentary, by Proposition 10 - (c). And R is the existential quantification of M. Thus R is an existential quantification of a rudimentary attribute.

The attribute M has the further properties:

(i) For every $x_1, \ldots, x_n, y$: $M(x_1, \ldots, x_n, y) \longrightarrow$

$$(y > x_1 \wedge \cdots \wedge y > x_n) \;.$$

(ii) For every $x_1, \ldots, x_n, y$: $M(x_1, \ldots, x_n, y) \longrightarrow U(y) = x_n$.

$$[U(y) \underset{df}{=} \theta\, L\, \theta(y) \text{ — cf. §12}].$$

Property (i) is obvious. As for (ii), suppose $M(x_1, \ldots, x_n, y)$. Then y pf $J(p, (x_1, \ldots, x_n)^{\#})$. Then $\theta y = J(p, (x_1, \ldots, x_n)^{\#})$. Then $L\theta y = (x_1, \ldots, x_n)^{\#}$. Then $\theta L \theta y = x_n$ — i.e., $U(y) = x_n$.

We also note that the function U is rudimentary, since for each x, $L(x) \leq x$ and $\theta(x) \leq x$, hence $U(x) = y$ iff $(Ex_1, x_2)_{\leq x}$ $[x_1 = \theta(x) \wedge x_2 = L(x_1) \wedge y = \theta(x_2)]$.

We have thus proved:

THEOREM 7. Every r.e. attribute $R(x_1, \ldots, x_n)$ is of the form $(Ey)M(x_1, \ldots, x_n, y)$ where M is rudimentary [a-fortiori, constructive arithmetic]. Moreover M can be chosen so that

(1) $M(x_1, \ldots, x_n, y) \longrightarrow (y > x_1 \wedge \cdots \wedge y > x_n)$

(2) $M(x_1, \ldots, x_n, y) \longrightarrow U(y) = x_n$.

DISCUSSION. It is now obvious that an attribute is r.e. (in the sense of this study) iff it is an existential quantification of a constructive arithmetic attribute. It follows readily from the work of Davis [5] or of Gödel [8] (using devices from number theory, like the Chinese remainder theorem) that an attribute is r.e. in the standard sense iff it is an existential quantification of a constructive arithmetic attribute. From these two facts it follows that our definition of "r.e." is indeed equivalent to the standard one. We could alternatively have proved the equivalence by using Post Canonical Systems.

We now see how recursive function theory can be made independent of number theory. We should like to remark that the methods of this section are by no means restricted in their application to the particular characterization of recursive enumerability in terms of elementary formal systems. It should be reasonably obvious to the reader familiar with other characterizations of recursivity how our techniques can be modified to obtain a direct proof of Theorem 7 for "r.e." defined in any of the more standard ways (e.g., in terms of primitive recursive functions, or the Gödel-Herbrand systems of recursion equations). Our essential work was done when we established Proposition 5.

FURTHER DISCUSSION. All of our results on rudimentary attributes can be strengthened as follows. We recall the notation "zPy" for "z is part of y (in dyadic notation)". Now let us introduce the notation:

$(Az)_{Py}R(x_1, \ldots, x_n, z)$ to mean $(Az)[zPy \supset R(x_1, \ldots, x_n, z)]$, and the analogous abbreviation: $(Ez)_{Py}R(x_1, \ldots, x_n, z)$ for $(Ez)[zPy \wedge R(x_1, \ldots, x_n, z)]$. These two quantifications are thus like the finite quantifications, except that the "part of" relation is used in place of the "less than". For the moment, let us refer to these quantifications as S-quantifications.[1] And let us define an S-rudimentary attribute as one like a rudimentary attribute except that the S-quantifications are used in place of the ordinary finite quantifications. We shall say that a function $f(x_1, \ldots, x_n)$ is S-progressing if the value of the function is not only greater than or equal to its arguments, but always contains its arguments as parts. It is a completely routine matter to check that all the results from Proposition 4 through Theorem 7 (excepting statement (f) of Proposition 4) remain valid if we replace "rudimentary" by "S-rudimentary" and "progressing" by "S-progressing".[2] [The proofs go through simply by always replacing "$<$" (or occassionally "$\leq$") by "P".] Also, the attribute M of Theorem 7 is such that $M(x_1, \ldots, x_m, y)$ implies not only that $x_1, \ldots, x_n$ are all less than y, but are all parts of y.

#C. ENUMERATION AND NORMAL FORM THEOREMS

§12. KLEENE ENUMERATION THEOREM

By applying Theorem 7 to the universal relation $U^n(z, x_1, \ldots, x_n)$ we obtain a rudimentary relation $M_n(z, x_1, \ldots, x_n, y)$ whose existential quantification is U^n, and M_n has the added properties (1), (2) of Theorem 7. We thus have:

THEOREM 8. [A strengthened form of Kleene's Enumeration Theorem.][3] For every r.e. relation $R(x_1, \ldots, x_n)$ a number i can be found; viz. an index of R, such that:

$$R(x_1, \ldots, x_n) \longleftrightarrow (Ey)M_n(i, x_1, \ldots, x_n, y) .$$

Stated otherwise:

$$R_i(x_1, \ldots, x_n) \longleftrightarrow (Ey)M_n(i, x_1, \ldots, x_n, y) .$$

[1] The letter "S" is used to suggest the term "syntactical", since the arithmetical significance of the dyadic numerals is now entirely lost; we might just as well be dealing with any two meaningless symbols in place of "1" and "2"

[2] This observation of the author has been independently verified by Robert Ritchie and by the author.

[3] This theorem was proved by Kleene [11] for a primitive recursive attribute T_n rather than a rudimentary attribute M_n.

Furthermore M_n has the properties:

(1) $M_n(i, x_1, \ldots, x_n, y) \longrightarrow y > i \quad y > x_1 \quad \ldots \quad y > x_n$.

(2) $M_n(i, x_1, \ldots, x_n, y) \longrightarrow U(y) = x_n$.

§13. SEPARATION OF DIFFERENCES OF r.e. SETS

The following well known principle — due to Rosser and Kleene — has important applications to recursive inseparability (cf. Chapter V).

For two r.e. sets ω_i, ω_j we shall say that $x \in \omega_i$ before $x \in \omega_j$ iff $(Ey)[M_1(i, x, y) \wedge (Ay')_{\leq y}[\tilde{M}_1(j, x, y')]]$. Let ω_i' be the set of all x such that $x \in \omega_i$ before $x \in \omega_j$; let ω_j' be the set of all x such that $x \in \omega_j$ before $x \in \omega_i$. It is obvious that ω_i', ω_j' are r.e. and disjoint, and that they are respective supersets of $(\omega_i - \omega_j)$, $(\omega_j - \omega_i)$. Thus for any two r.e. sets ω_i, ω_j, there exists disjoint r.e. supersets of $(\omega_i - \omega_j)$, $(\omega_j - \omega_i)$.

§14. PARTIAL RECURSIVE FUNCTIONS

For two partial functions $q_1(x_1, \ldots, x_n)$ and $q_2(x_1, \ldots, x_n)$ we write (after Kleene) $q_1(x_1, \ldots, x_n) \simeq q_2(x_1, \ldots, x_n)$ to mean that either $q_1(x_1, \ldots, x_n)$ and $q_2(x_1, \ldots, x_n)$ are both defined and have the same value or they are both undefined.

For any relation $R(x_1, \ldots, x_n, y)$, by $(\mu y)R(x_1, \ldots, x_n, y)$ we shall mean the smallest y for which $R(x_1, \ldots, x_n, y)$ if there is one; otherwise the expression is to be undefined. For any function f, $f(\mu y)R(x_1, \ldots, x_n, y)$ is a partial function which only has values for those n-tuples $(x_1, \ldots, x_n)$ for which $(Ey)R(x_1, \ldots, x_n, y)$.

For any r.e. relation $R_i(x_1, \ldots, x_n, x)$, by the first x such that $R_i(x_1, \ldots, x_n, x)$ — which we write $q_i(x_1, \ldots, x_n)$ — we mean not the smallest such x, but rather that x (if there is one) such that for some y, $M_{n+1}(i, x_1, \ldots, x_n, x, y)$ holds but for no smaller y' is there an x' such that $M_{n+1}(i, x_1, \ldots, x_n, x', y')$. Since $M_{n+1}(i, x_1, \ldots, x_n, x, y) \longrightarrow x = U(y)$, then it is obvious that $q_i(x_1, \ldots, x_n) = x \longleftrightarrow x = U(\mu y)M_{n+1}(i, x_1, \ldots, x_n, U(y), y)$. Stated otherwise: $q_i(x_1, \ldots, x_n) \simeq U(\mu y)M_{n+1}(i, x_1, \ldots, x_n, U(y), y)$.

We recall that we are identifying a partial function $\varphi(x_1, \ldots, x_n)$ with the relation consisting of the set of all $n + 1$ tuples $(x_1, \ldots, x_n, x)$ such that $\varphi(x_1, \ldots, x_n) = x$. Thus if a r.e. relation $R_i(x_1, \ldots, x_n, x)$ is single valued, in the sense that for all $x_1, \ldots, x_n$ there is at most one x such that $R(x_1, \ldots, x_n, x)$, then R_i can be looked at as a partial recursive function. And if R_i is a partial recursive function, then R_i is the same as q_i stated otherwise: If R_i is single valued, then $R_i(x_1, \ldots, x_n, x) \longleftrightarrow q_i(x_1, \ldots, x_n) = x$. If R_i is not single valued, then $q_i \subseteq R_i$ — i.e., the set of all $(x_1, \ldots, x_n, x)$ such that $q_i(x_1, \ldots, x_n) = x$ is a sub-relation of R_i. Then $q_i = R_j$ for some j and $R_j \subseteq R_i$. We remark that j can be effectively found from i, as we shall soon see.

We abbreviate "$M_{n+1}(z, x_1, \ldots, x_n, U(y), y))$" by "$S_n(z, x_1, \ldots, x_n, y)$". And we define (as in Kleene) $T_n(z, x_1, \ldots, x_n, y) \longleftrightarrow S_n(z, x_1, \ldots, x_n, y) \wedge (Ay')_{<y} \tilde{S}_n(z, x_1, \ldots, x_n, y')$. It is clear that T_n is rudimentary. And it is clear that $(Ey)S_n(z, x_1, \ldots, x_n, y) \longleftrightarrow (Ey)T_n(z, x_1, \ldots, x_n, y)$, and that $U(\mu y)T_n(z, x_1, \ldots, x_n, y) \simeq U(\mu y)S_n(z, x_1, \ldots, x_n, y)$. Thus $q_i(x_1, \ldots, x_n) \simeq U(\mu y)T_n(i, x_1, \ldots, x_n, y)$. As pointed out by Kleene, the advantage of using T_n in place of S_n is that it is always the case that $T_n(i, x_1, \ldots, x_n, y) \longrightarrow q_i(x_1, \ldots, x_n) = U(y)$, whereas if R_i is not single valued, then it is not always true that $S_n(i, x_1, \ldots, x_n, y) \longrightarrow q_i(x_1, \ldots, x_n) = U(y)$ [though it is of course true that $S_n(i, x_1, \ldots, x_n, y) \longrightarrow R_i(x_1, \ldots, x_n, U(y))$].

We have now proved:

THEOREM 9 [An extension of Kleene's Normal Form Theorem].[1] The rudimentary relation T_n and the rudimentary function U have the properties:

(1) Every partial recursive function $q(x_1, \ldots, x_n)$ is of the form $q_i(x_1, \ldots, x_n)$; i.e., $U(\mu y)T_n(i, x_1, \ldots, x_n, y)$.

(2) $T_n(i, x_1, \ldots, x_n, y) \longrightarrow U(y) = q_i(x_1, \ldots, x_n)$.

§15. FUNCTIONAL INDEXING

What we have so far termed an index i of an r.e. relation R_i, let us now (for emphasis) call an r.e. index. Thus i is an r.e. index of R_i. We shall call i a functional index of the partial recursive function $q_i(x_1, \ldots, x_n)$. If R_i is single valued, then i is both an r.e. index and a functional index of R_i (i.e., of q_i). So it is a trivial matter to pass from an r.e. index i of an r.e. relation $q(x_1, \ldots, x_n) = x$ to a functional index of q (for then $q = q_i$). Suppose now that i is a functional index of q_i; how do we effectively obtain an r.e. index $\varphi(i)$ of the relation $q_i(x_1, \ldots, x_n) = x$? Well, let $L(z, x_1, \ldots, x_n, x)$ be the r.e. relation

[1] This was proved by Kleene for a primitive recursive U and T_n rather than a rudimentary U and T_n.

$q_z(x_1, \ldots, x_n) = x$ [this relation is r.e., for it can be put in the form: $(Ey)T_n(z, x_1, \ldots, x_n, y) \wedge x = U(y)$]]. Then by the iteration theorem there is a recursive function $\varphi(z)$ such that for every i, $\varphi(i)$ is an index of L_i — i.e., of the relation $q_i(x_1, \ldots, x_n) = x$. This proves:

THEOREM 10. There is a recursive function $\varphi(z)$ such that for all i, $q_i = R_{\varphi(i)}$ — for all $i, x_1, \ldots, x_n, x$:

$$q_i(x_1, \ldots, x_n) = x \longleftrightarrow R_{\varphi(i)}(x_1, \ldots, x_n, x) .$$

DISCUSSION. We have already remarked that Kleene's S_n^m theorem can be looked at as a special case of the iteration theorem (Theorem 2) and that Kleene's second recursion theorem can be obtained from Theorem 4.1 [Fixed Point Theorem]. Let us now establish this explicitly.

(1) Let us consider the r.e. relation $q_z(z_1, \ldots, z_n, x_1, \ldots, x_m) = x$ [this now is a relation of all the variables $z, z_1, \ldots, z_n, x_1, \ldots, x_m, x$)]. By the iteration theorem there is a (primitive) recursive function $S_n^m(z, z_1, \ldots, z_n)$ such that for all numbers $e, i_1, \ldots, i_n$, $S_n^m(e, i_1, \ldots, i_n)$ is a <u>r.e.</u> index of the relation $q_e(i_1, \ldots, i_n, x_1, \ldots, x_m) = x$. But such an index is also a <u>functional</u> index of the partial recursive function $q_e(i_1, \ldots, i_n, x_1, \ldots, x_n)$ [as a function of the arguments $x_1, \ldots, x_n$]. This is precisely Kleene's S_n^m theorem.

(2) Consider the r.e. relation $q_z(y, x_1, \ldots, x_n) = x$. By Theorem 4.1 there is a recursive function $t(x)$ such that for all i, $t(i)$ is a r.e. index of the relation $q_i(t(i), x_1, \ldots, x_n) = x$. But then $t(i)$ is also a functional index of the partial recursive function $q_i(t(i), x_1, \ldots, x_n)$ [as a function of $x_1, \ldots, x_n$]. This is Kleene's second recursion theorem.

We remark that from Theorem 5 (in place of Theorem 4.1) we can similarly prove a "double analogue" of the Kleene recursion theorem; viz. "For any two partial recursive functions $g_1(z, x_1, \ldots, x_n)$, $g_2(z, x_1, \ldots, x_n)$ a number e can be found such that $K(e)$ is an index of $g_1(e, x_1, \ldots, x_n)$ and $L(e)$ is an index of $g_2(e, x_1, \ldots, x_n)$."

<u>Note to Chapter IV</u> [Added in second printing]. Dr. Richard Bennett has recently proved that the class of constructive arithmetic attributes is identical with the class of rudimentary attributes. Still more remarkable, he showed that the exponential relation $x^y = z$ is rudimentary. He also showed that the S-rudimentary attributes form a strictly smaller class than the rudimentary attributes — in fact the relation $x + y = z$, though rudimentary, is not S-rudimentary. These results are contained in Bennett's Doctoral Dissertation "On Spectra," Princeton, May 1962.

CHAPTER V. CREATIVITY AND EFFECTIVE INSEPARABILITY

#A. CREATIVITY AND EFFECTIVE INSEPARABILITY

§1. PRODUCTIVE AND CREATIVE SETS; RECURSIVE AND EFFECTIVE INSEPARABILITY

We consider the sequence $\omega_1, \omega_2, \ldots, \omega_i, \ldots$ of all r.e. sets arranged as in the Post enumeration (cf. #A, Chapter IV). A number set α is called productive iff there is a recursive function $\varphi(x)$ such that for every r.e. subset ω_i of α, $\varphi(i) \in \alpha - \omega_i$; such a function $\varphi(x)$ is called a productive function for α. Post calls a set α creative iff α is r.e. and $\tilde{\alpha}$ is productive. Thus α is creative iff α is r.e. and there exists a recursive function $\varphi(x)$ such that for every number i for which ω_i is disjoint from α, $\varphi(i)$ is outside both α and ω_i.

A simple example of a creative set C [after Post] is the set of all x such that $x \in \omega_x$. Let $\varphi(x)$ be the identity function (which is certainly recursive). Then for any number i, $i \in C \longleftrightarrow i \in \omega_i$ [by definition of C]. Hence $\varphi(i) \in C \longleftrightarrow \varphi(i) \in \omega_i$. If ω_i is disjoint from C, then $\varphi(i) \notin (C \cup \omega_i)$. Hence $\varphi(x)$ is a productive function for $\tilde{C}$.

We note that C has the stronger property that there exists a recursive function $\varphi(x)$ — viz. the identity function — such that for any r.e. set ω_i, whether disjoint from C or not, $\varphi(i)$ is either in both C and ω_i or is outside both C and ω_i. Such a set C is called completely creative by J. Dekker.[1] From Myhill's result — that any two creative sets are isomorphic — it follows that every creative set is completely creative. [We prove Myhill's result in #B.]

RECURSIVE INSEPARABILITY. We have remarked in Chapter III that one way to obtain an R.I. (recursively inseparable) pair of r.e. sets is to take the nuclei (T_o, R_o) of a formal consistent Rosser system (or even of a

[1] Or rather he calls its complement "completely productive".

formal system in which all recursive sets are definable — cf. Chapter III #C). This might be called a "metamathematical" approach. We now consider a more direct method due to Kleene. This method suggests an interesting principal — purely set-theoretic in nature — which we shall first study in its full generality.

We let $A_1, A_2, \ldots, A_i, \ldots$ be a denumerable sequence of sets of numbers; Σ is the collection of all sets A_i and Σ^x is the collection of all those sets A_i whose complement $\tilde{A}_i$ is also in Σ. For two disjoint number sets A and B, we shall say that A is separable from B in the collection Σ^x iff there is a superset A' of A which is disjoint from B and which is in Σ^x. This is obviously equivalent to the condition that some superset B' of B disjoint from A is in Σ^x. Thus A is separable from B in Σ^x iff B is separable from A in Σ^x. We say that the pair (A, B) is inseparable in Σ^x iff A is not separable from B in Σ^x.

We let $J(x, y)$ be a $1 - 1$ function from the set of all ordered pairs of numbers into the set of numbers (for the time being, J does not have to be recursive). For any number x of the form $J(x_1, x_2)$ we let $(x)_1 = x_1$ and $(x)_2 = x_2$; for x is not of this form, $(x)_1$ and $(x)_2$ can be arbitrary. We now define the sets κ_1, κ_2 by the following conditions:

$$x \in \kappa_1 \Longleftrightarrow x \in A_{(x)_1}$$

$$x \in \kappa_2 \Longleftrightarrow x \in A_{(x)_2} \quad .$$

The following lemma underlies Kleene's construction of R.I. sets.

LEMMA [Symmetric Lemma]. The sets $(\kappa_1 - \kappa_2), (\kappa_2 - \kappa_1)$ are inseparable in the collection Σ^x. In fact if A_i, A_j are elements of Σ which are respective supersets of $(\kappa_1 - \kappa_2), (\kappa_2 - \kappa_1)$, and if $k = J(j, i)$ then $k \in A_i \Longleftrightarrow k \in A_j$. Hence if A_i, A_j are furthermore disjoint, then $k \notin A_i$ and $k \notin A_j$, so A_j is not the complement of A_i.

PROOF.

(1) $k \in \kappa_1 \Longleftrightarrow k \in A_j$ [by definition of κ_1]

(2) $k \in \kappa_2 \Longleftrightarrow k \in A_i$ [by definition of κ_2]

Hence:

(3) $k \in (A_j - A_i) \Longleftrightarrow k \in (\kappa_1 - \kappa_2)$ [by (1) and (2)]
$\Longrightarrow k \in A_i$ [since $(\kappa_1 - \kappa_2) \subseteq A_i$]

(4) $k \in (A_i - A_j) \Longleftrightarrow k \in (\kappa_2 - \kappa_1)$ [by (1) and (2)]
$\Longrightarrow k \in A_j$ [since $(\kappa_2 - \kappa_1) \subseteq A_j$] .

By (3) $k \notin (A_j - A_i)$; by (4) $k \notin (A_i - A_j)$

Hence $k \in A_i \longleftrightarrow k \in A_j$.

We now apply the symmetric lemma to the sequence $\omega_1, \omega_2, \ldots, \omega_i \ldots$ of all r.e. sets, arranged in the Post enumeration (cf. §2, Chapter IV). Σ^x is now the class of all recursive sets. We let $J(x, y)$ be a 1 - 1 function (for the moment not necessarily recursive); we define the sets κ_1, κ_2 accordingly, and the symmetric lemma then says that the sets $(\kappa_1 - \kappa_2), (\kappa_2 - \kappa_1)$ are recursively inseparable (i.e., not separable in Σ^x).

Let us now take $J(x, y)$ to be a recursive function, say the function $J(x, y)$ defined in Chapter IV and take $x_{(1)}$ to be $K(x)$; $x_{(2)}$ to be $L(x)$. It is then obvious that κ_1 and κ_2 are each r.e. sets $[x \in \kappa_1 \longleftrightarrow x \in \omega_{Kx} \longleftrightarrow U(x, Kx) \longleftrightarrow (Ey)[y = Kx \wedge U(x, y)]$; similarly $x \in \kappa_2 \longleftrightarrow (Ey)[y = Lx \wedge U(x, y)]$.]

It then follows (cf. §13, Chapter IV) that there exists disjoint r.e. sets κ_1', κ_2' such that $(\kappa_1 - \kappa_2) \subseteq \kappa_1'$; $(\kappa_2 - \kappa_1) \subseteq \kappa_2'$. Since the smaller pair $[(\kappa_1 - \kappa_2), (\kappa_2 - \kappa_1)]$ is R.I., then the larger pair $[\kappa_1', \kappa_2']$ is likewise R.I. We thus have a pair (κ_1', κ_2') of R.I. sets each of which is r.e. We shall refer to these sets as the <u>Kleene</u> sets.

EFFECTIVE INSEPARABILITY. A pair (A, B) of disjoint number sets is called <u>effectively inseparable</u> (abbreviated "E.I.") iff there is a recursive function $\delta(x, y)$ such that for every disjoint pair (ω_i, ω_j) of r.e. supersets of (A, B) [in respective order], $\delta(i, j)$ is an element outside both ω_i and ω_j. Such a function $\delta(x, y)$ we shall call an <u>E.I. function</u> for the pair (A, B). If we let $\delta'(x, y) \underset{df}{=} \delta(y, x)$, then it is obvious that δ' is recursive iff δ is recursive, and that δ is an E.I. function for (A, B) iff δ' is an E.I. function for (B, A). Hence the condition "(A, B) is E.I." is symmetric in A and B.

Consider now the sets κ_1, κ_2 above. The sets $(\kappa_1 - \kappa_2)$, $(\kappa_2 - \kappa_1)$ are not only R.I. but E.I., because if ω_i, ω_j are disjoint r.e. supersets of $(\kappa_1 - \kappa_2), (\kappa_2 - \kappa_1)$ respectively, then $J(j, i)$ is outside both ω_i and ω_j (by the symmetric lemma). Thus $J(x, y)$ is an E.I. function for $((\kappa_2 - \kappa_1), (\kappa_1 - \kappa_2))$. Since the smaller sets $(\kappa_1 - \kappa_2), (\kappa_2 - \kappa_1)$ are E.I., so are the larger sets κ_1', κ_2'. Thus the Kleene sets are r.e. sets which are E.I.

§2. MANY-ONE AND ONE-ONE REDUCIBILITY

A recursive function $f(x)$ is called a (many-one) <u>reduction</u> of α to β iff $\alpha = f^{-1}(\beta)$. [Equivalently iff f maps α into β and

$\tilde{\alpha}$ into $\tilde{\beta}$; or equivalently iff for every number x, $x \in \alpha \longleftrightarrow f(x) \in \beta$]. If in addition f is $1 - 1$, then f is called a $1 - 1$ reduction of α to β. The set α is called (many-one) reducible to β iff there exists an f which is a (many-one) reduction of α to β; similarly with "$1 - 1$ reducible". We write "$\alpha R_m \beta$" for "α is (many-one) reducible to β" and "$\alpha R_1 \beta$" for "α is $1 - 1$ reducible to β". It is obvious that if $f(x)$ is a reduction of α to β then $f(x)$ is also a reduction of $\tilde{\alpha}$ to $\tilde{\beta}$. If α and β are each $1 - 1$ reducible to each other, then they are called "$1 - 1$ equivalent", and we write "$\alpha \underset{1}{\equiv} \beta$". If there exists a recursive <u>permutation</u> $\varphi(x)$ of the integers (i.e., a $1 - 1$ recursive function from N <u>onto</u> N) which is a $1 - 1$ reduction of α to β, then α and β are called <u>isomorphic</u>; in symbols: $\alpha \cong \beta$. Clearly if $\varphi(x)$ is an isomorphism from α to β, then $\varphi(x)$ maps α <u>onto</u> β (and $\tilde{\alpha}$ <u>onto</u> $\tilde{\beta}$). It is also obvious that the relation "$\alpha \cong \beta$", is an equivalence relation. Lastly it is obvious that if $\alpha \cong \beta$ then $\alpha \underset{1}{\equiv} \beta$ (and also that $\beta \underset{1}{\equiv} \alpha$).

We first consider the following preliminary proposition.

PROPOSITION 1. Let $\alpha R_m \beta$. Then

(a) if β is r.e. so is α.
(b) If $\tilde{\beta}$ is r.e. so is $\tilde{\alpha}$.
(c) If β is recursive so is α.

PROOF. Let $g(x)$ be a (many-one) reduction of α to β. Then $\alpha = g^{-1}(\beta)$ and $\tilde{\alpha} = g^{-1}(\tilde{\beta})$. Result then follows from Theorem 1, Corollary 1, Chapter II.

Myhill and Dekker have shown that if $\alpha R_m \beta$ and if α is productive (creative) then β is productive (respectively creative, providing β is r.e.). We shall need the stronger statement:

PROPOSITION 2.

(a) If f is a reduction of α to β, if $g(x)$ is a productive function for $\tilde{\alpha}$, if $t(x)$ is a recursive function such that for every i, $\omega_{t(i)} = f^{-1}(\omega_i)$, then $fgt(x)$ is a productive function for $\tilde{\beta}$.

(b) For every set α whose complement is productive and for every recursive function $f(x)$, a recursive function $f'(x)$ can be found such that for every set β, if f is a reduction of α to β then f' is a productive function for $\tilde{\beta}$.

(c) Let $\alpha R_m \beta$. Then if α is productive so is β. If $\tilde{\alpha}$ is productive so is $\tilde{\beta}$. If α is creative and β is r.e. then β is creative.

PROOF. (a) We are assuming:

(1) $g(x)$ is productive for $\tilde{\alpha}$.

(2) $\omega_{t(i)} = f^{-1}(\omega_i)$ [for every i].

(3) f is a reduction of α to β.

Let ω_i be any r.e. set disjoint from β. Then $f^{-1}(\omega_i)$ is disjoint from $f^{-1}(\beta)$. Then $\omega_{t(i)}$ is disjoint from α [since $\omega_{t(i)} = f^{-1}(\omega_i)$ and $\alpha = f^{-1}(\beta)$, by (2) and (3) respectively]. Then $gti \notin \alpha \cup \omega_{t(i)}$ [by (1)]. Hence $gt(i) \notin \alpha$ and $gti \notin \omega_{t(i)}$. And since f maps $\tilde{\alpha}$ into $\tilde{\beta}$ and $\tilde{\omega}_{t(i)}$ into $\tilde{\omega}_i$ (i.e., $f^{-1}(\omega_i)$ into $\tilde{\omega}_i$), then $fgt(i) \notin \beta$ and $fgt(i) \notin \omega_i$ — i.e., $fgt(i) \notin \beta \cup \omega_i$. Thus we have proved: ω_i disjoint from $\beta \longrightarrow fgt(i) \notin \beta \cup \omega_i$. And $fgt(x)$ is a recursive function (since f, g, and t are). Therefore $fgt(x)$ is a productive function for $\tilde{\beta}$.

(b) Immediate from (a) and the fact that for any recursive function f there is a recursive function t such that for all i, $\omega_{t(i)} = f^{-1}(\omega_i)$.

(c) Immediate from (b).

COROLLARY 1. [Myhill, Dekker]. If every r.e. set is reducible to α, then $\tilde{\alpha}$ is productive.

PROOF. By Proposition 2(c) and the existence of a creative set.

§3. CREATIVE SYSTEMS

A representation system Q will be called <u>creative</u> iff T_o is a creative set and <u>productive</u> iff T_o is a productive set.

PROPOSITION 3. If A is representable in Q, then A is reducible to T_o.

PROOF. $H_T = \varphi_h^{-1}(T_o)$, so φ_h is a reduction of H_T to T_o. If A is representable in Q then for some H, $A = H_T$, so A is then reducible to T_o.

From Propositions 2 and 3 immediately follows:

THEOREM 1. (a) [Myhill]. If some creative set is representable in Q and Q is formal, then Q is creative.

(b) If some productive set is representable in Q then Q is productive.

From which in turn follows:

THEOREM 2. (a) [Myhill]. If all r.e. sets are representable in Q and Q is formal, then Q is creative.

(b) If the complement of every r.e. set is representable in Q then Q is productive.

PROOF. By Theorem 1 and the existence of a creative set.

§4. EFFECTIVE INSEPARABILITY

We now need "effective" analogues of Propositions 4 and 6 — Chapter III.

PROPOSITION 4. Let $(A_1, A_2) \xrightarrow[f]{} (B_1, B_2)$, for f recursive; let (B_1, B_2) be disjoint. Then if (A_1, A_2) is E.I. so is (B_1, B_2).

PROOF. We have shown in Chapter IV, §4 — that for any number i we can effectively find an index $\varphi(i)$ of $f^{-1}(\omega_i)$ — i.e., there is a recursive function $\varphi(x)$ such that for every i, $\omega_{\varphi(i)} = f^{-1}(\omega_i)$.

Let $\delta(x, y)$ be an E.I. function for (A_1, A_2). Define $\delta'(x, y) \underset{df}{=} f\delta[\varphi(x), \varphi(y)]$. We assert that δ' is an E.I. function for (B_1, B_2).

Suppose $B \subseteq \omega_i$; $B_2 \subseteq \omega_j$ and ω_i, ω_j are disjoint. Then $A_1 \subseteq f^{-1}(\omega_i)$; $A_2 \subseteq f^{-1}(\omega_j)$ and $f^{-1}(\omega_i)$, $f^{-1}(\omega_j)$ are disjoint. Thus $A_1 \subseteq \omega_{\varphi(i)}$, $A_2 \subseteq \omega_{\varphi(j)}$ and $\omega_{\varphi(i)}$, $\omega_{\varphi(j)}$ are disjoint. Then $\delta(\varphi(i), \varphi(j)) \notin (\omega_{\varphi(i)} \cup \omega_{\varphi(j)})$ [since δ is an E.I. function for (A_1, A_2)]. Thus $\delta[\varphi(i), \varphi(j)] \notin f^{-1}(\omega_i)$ and $\delta[\varphi(i), \varphi(j)] \notin f^{-1}(\omega_j)$. So $f\delta[\varphi(i), \varphi(j)]$ is outside both ω_i and ω_j — i.e., $\delta'(i, j)$ is outside both ω_i and ω_j, which was to be proved.

COROLLARY 1. For any recursive function f and any disjoint number sets (A, B) if $(f^{-1}(A), f^{-1}(B))$ is E.I. so is (A, B).

PROPOSITION 5. For any disjoint sets W and V of expressions of Q:

(a) If (W^*, V^*) is E.I. so is $((\vec{W})_0, (\vec{V})_0)$ — a-fortiori so is (W_0, V_0).

(b) For any predicate H of Q:

$$(H_W, H_V) \text{ is E.I.} \longrightarrow (W_0, V_0) \text{ is E.I.}$$

PROOF. By Proposition 5 of Chapter III (§19), $(W^*, V^*) \xrightarrow{f} (\vec{W}_0, \vec{V}_0)$ and $(H_W, H_V) \xrightarrow[g]{} (W_0, V_0)$ for recursive functions f and g. Result then follows by Proposition 4 above.

PROPOSITION 6. If A is strongly separable from B within Z, then $(A, B) \xrightarrow[f]{} (T_0, R_0)$, for a recursive function f.

PROOF. Let H strongly separate A from B within Z. Then $A \subseteq H_T$; $B \subseteq H_R$. Also $H_T = \varphi_h^{-1}(T_0)$; $H_R = \varphi_h^{-1}(R_0)$, so $A \subseteq \varphi_h^{-1}(T_0)$; $B \subseteq \varphi_h^{-1}(R_0)$. Hence $(A, B) \xrightarrow[\varphi_h]{} (T_0, R_0)$, and φ_h is recursive.

THEOREM 3. [An extension of Kleene's symmetric Form of Gödel's Theorem.] If (A, B) is effectively inseparable but strongly separable in a consistent theory Z, then the nuclei T_o, R_o of Z are in turn effectively inseparable.

PROOF. Let (A, B) be E.I. and let (A, B) be strongly separable in Z. Then by Proposition 6, $(A, B) \xrightarrow[f]{} (T_o, R_o)$ for a recursive function f. By the assumption of consistency, T_o, R_o are disjoint. Then (T_o, R_o) is E.I. by Proposition 4.

THEOREM 4. If Z is a consistent Rosser system then its nuclei T_o, R_o are effectively inseparable.

PROOF. Result is immediate from Theorem 3 and the fact that there exists a pair of r.e. sets (A, B) which is E.I. Such a pair must then be strongly separable in Z, by the hypothesis that Z is a Rosser system.

§5. EFFECTIVE ROSSER SYSTEMS

We shall say that Z is <u>effectively</u> a Rosser system iff there is a recursive function $r(x, y)$ — which we call a <u>Rosser function</u> for Z — such that for any two disjoint r.e. sets ω_i, ω_j, $r(i, j)$ is the Gödel number of some predicate of Z which strongly separates ω_i from ω_j.

We already know that if Z is a consistent Rosser system then its nuclei T_o, R_o are E.I. Can we obtain any stronger conclusion under the added assumption that Z is <u>effectively</u> a Rosser system? Our next theorem provides one such conclusion.

THEOREM 5. If Z is consistent and effectively a Rosser system, then its diagonal sets T^*, R^* (and hence also the sets $(\vec{T})_o$, $(\vec{R})_o$) are effectively inseparable.

PROOF. Let $r(x, y)$ be a Rosser function for Z. We show (under the assumption that Z is consistent) that $r(x, y)$ is also an E.I. function for (R^*, T^*).

Let ω_i, ω_j be disjoint r.e. supersets of R^*, T^*, let $h = r(i, j)$. By hypothesis, h is the Gödel number of a predicate H which strongly separates ω_i from ω_j. Then H strongly separates R^* from T^*. Then by Theorem 5, Chapter III, Hh is undecidable in Z (since Z is consistent). This means that $Hh \notin T$ and $Hh \notin R$. Hence $h \notin H_T$ and $h \notin H_R$. Now H_T, H_R are respective supersets of ω_i, ω_j (since H strongly separates ω_i from ω_j in Z). Therefore $h \notin \omega_i$ and $h \notin \omega_j$ — i.e., $r(i, j) \notin (\omega_i \cup \omega_j)$. Therefore $r(x, y)$ is an E.I. function for (R^*, T^*), so (R^*, T^*) is E.I.

#B. FURTHER THEORY OF PRODUCTIVE SETS

In this section we establish some deeper results concerning productive and creative sets.

§6. WEAKLY PRODUCTIVE FUNCTIONS

We shall call a recursive function $g(x)$ a <u>weakly productive</u> function for α iff for every number i the following conditions hold:

(1) If ω_i is empty then $g(i) \in \alpha$.

(2) If ω_i is a unit set contained in α then $g(i) \notin \omega_i$.

It is obvious that if $g(x)$ is a productive function for α then it is a weakly productive function for α.

We note that $g(x)$ is a weakly productive function for $\tilde{\alpha}$ iff for every number i:

(1) If ω_i is empty then $g(i) \notin \alpha$.

(2) If ω_i is a unit set disjoint from α then $g(i) \notin \omega_i$.

We will soon show that if α is a weakly productive (i.e., if α possesses a weakly productive function) then α is productive.

Myhill has proved (Theorem 10, [14]) that if α is creative then every r.e. set is reducible to it. By a slight modification of Myhill's argument we obtain a stronger result which will have several new applications.

THEOREM 6. [After Myhill]. Let A be a fixed r.e. set. Then

(a) For every recursive function $g(x)$ there is a recursive function $f(x)$ such that for every set α the following condition holds: If $g(x)$ is a productive <u>or even a weakly productive</u> function for $\tilde{\alpha}$, then $f(x)$ is a reduction of A to α. [Equivalently, if $g(x)$ is a weakly productive function for α, then $f(x)$ is a reduction of $\tilde{A}$ to α.]

(b) More strongly: Let α, A, $g(x)$, $t(x)$ satisfy the following conditions:

(i) For every $i \in A$, $t(i)$ is an index of $\{gt(i)\}$; for every $i \notin A$, $t(i)$ is an index of the empty set.

(ii) $t(x)$ is recursive.

(iii) $g(x)$ is weakly productive for $\tilde{\alpha}$.

Then $gt(x)$ is a reduction of A to α.

PROOF. We first note that (a) is a consequence of (b), since the existence of a recursive function $t(x)$ satisfying conditions (i) and

(ii) in (b) is guaranteed by Theorem 4.4 — Chapter IV. So we prove (b).

Assume now that conditions (i), (ii), (iii) of (b) are satisfied.

1. Suppose $i \in A$. Then $\omega_{t(i)} = \{gt(i)\}$. Suppose $gt(i) \notin \alpha$. Then $\omega_{t(i)}$ is disjoint from α. Since $g(x)$ is a weakly productive function for $\tilde{\alpha}$, it then follows that $gt(i) \notin \omega_{t(i)}$. This means that $gt(i) \notin \{gt(i)\}$, which is absurd. Hence $i \in A \longrightarrow gt(i) \in \alpha$.

2. Suppose $i \notin A$. Then $\omega_{t(i)}$ is empty. Then again, since $g(x)$ is weakly productive for $\tilde{\alpha}$, $gt(i) \notin \alpha$. Hence $i \notin A \longrightarrow gt(i) \notin \alpha$.

By (1) and (2), $gt(x)$ is a reduction of A to α.

COROLLARY 1. If $\tilde{\alpha}$ is weakly productive then every r.e. set is many-one reducible to α. A-fortiori if $\tilde{\alpha}$ is productive then every r.e. set is many-one reducible to α.

COROLLARY 2. If α is weakly productive then α is productive.

PROOF. Suppose α is weakly productive. Then every r.e. set is reducible to $\tilde{\alpha}$ (by Corollary 1). Hence α is productive, by Prop. 2 - Cor. 1.

COROLLARY 3. Let Σ be a non empty collection of sets which have a common weakly productive function $g(x)$ [i.e., for each element $\alpha \in \Sigma$, $g(x)$ is a weakly productive function for α]. Then

(a) The elements of Σ possess a common productive function.

(b) The intersection of all elements of Σ is productive.

(c) The union of all elements of Σ is productive.

PROOF. (a) Let A be a creative set; construct $f(x)$ from A and $g(x)$ as in Theorem 6. Construct $f'(x)$ from $f(x)$ and A as in Proposition 2 (b). We assert that $f'(x)$ is a productive function for all elements of Σ.

Let α be any element of Σ. By hypothesis $g(x)$ is a weakly productive function for α. Then by Theorem 6, $f(x)$ is a reduction of $\tilde{A}$ to α. Then by Proposition 2, $f'(x)$ is a productive function for α. Since α is <u>any</u> element of Σ, statement (a) is established.

(b), (c). Let S be the intersection (respectively union) of all elements of Σ. Since the function $f(x)$ is a reduction of $\tilde{A}$ to every element of Σ, then it is obviously a reduction of $\tilde{A}$ to S. Hence $\tilde{A}$ is reducible to S, so S is productive, by Proposition 2 (c).

REMARKS. It is immediate from Corollary 3 (b) that two disjoint sets cannot possess a common productive (or even weakly productive) function, since the empty set is obviously not productive. It also follows from Corollary 3 (c) that if Σ is a collection of r.e. sets whose complements have a common productive — or even weakly productive function — then the intersection S of all elements of Σ is creative.

§7. UNIFORM REDUCIBILITY

Let Σ be a collection of r.e. sets and let α be a fixed set. We say that all elements of Σ are uniformly reducible to α, or that the elements of Σ are reducible to α in a uniform manner iff there is a recursive function $f(x, y)$ such that for every i for which $\omega_i \in \Sigma$, f_i is a reduction of ω_i to α — i.e., for all numbers x, $x \in \omega_i \longleftrightarrow f(i, x) \in \alpha$. [We recall the notation: $f_i(x) = f(i, x)$.] Such a function is to be called a uniform reduction of Σ to α.

We shall also say that α is uniformly reducible to all elements of Σ, or that α is reducible to all elements of Σ in a uniform manner iff there is a recursive function $g(x, y)$ such that for every number i for which $\omega_i \in \Sigma$, g_i is a reduction of α to ω_i.

UNIFORM CREATIVITY. Again let Σ be a collection of r.e. sets. We shall say that the elements of Σ are uniformly creative (uniformly weakly creative) or that they are creative (weakly creative) in a uniform manner iff there is a recursive function $g(x, y)$ such that for every i for which $\omega_i \in \Sigma$, g_i is a productive (respectively weakly productive) function for $\tilde{\omega}_i$. [We again use the notation: $g_i(y) \underset{df}{=} g(i, y)$.] This intuitively means that there is an effective process whereby given any index i of an element ω_i of Σ, we can "find" a productive function g_i for $\tilde{\omega}_i$. If $g(x, y)$ is a recursive function satisfying the above requirements then we shall say that the elements of Σ are uniformly creative under the function $g(x, y)$.

LEMMA. For any recursive function $f(x, y)$ there is a recursive function $t(x, y)$ such that for every pair of numbers i, j we have:

$$\omega_{t_i(j)} = f_i^{-1}(\omega_j) \quad .$$

PROOF. Let $M(z_1, z_2, x)$ be the relation: $(Ey)[f(z_1, x) = y \wedge y \in \omega_{z_2}]$. M is certainly r.e. By the iteration theorem there is a recursive function $t(x, y)$ such that for every i, j, x:

$$x \in \omega_{t(i,j)} \longleftrightarrow M(i, j, x) \ .$$

Hence we have:

$$
\begin{aligned}
x \in \omega_{t_i(j)} &\longleftrightarrow x \in \omega_{t(i,j)} \\
&\longleftrightarrow M(i, j, x) \\
&\longleftrightarrow (Ey)[f(i, x) = y \wedge y \in \omega_j] \\
&\longleftrightarrow (Ey)[f_i(x) = y \wedge y \in \omega_j] \\
&\longleftrightarrow x \in f_i^{-1}(\omega_j) \ .
\end{aligned}
$$

Hence $\omega_{t_i(j)} = f_i^{-1}(\omega_j)$.

THEOREM 7. If $\tilde{A}$ is productive and if A is uniformly reducible to all elements of Σ, then all elements of Σ are uniformly creative.

PROOF. Let $f(x, y)$ uniformly reduce A to all elements of Σ. Let $t(x, y)$ be as in the preceding lemma. Let $g(x)$ be a productive function for $\tilde{A}$. Let i be any number such that $\omega_i \in \Sigma$. Then we have:

(1) f_i reduces A to ω_i .

(2) $g(x)$ is productive for $\tilde{A}$.

(3) For every number j, $\omega_{t_i(j)} = f_i^{-1}(\omega_j)$.

Then by Proposition 2 (a) [reading "t_i" for "t", "j" for "i" and "f_i" for "f"], $f_i g t_i(y)$ is a productive function for $\tilde{\omega}_i$. We hence define $h(x, y) = f[x, gt(x, y)]$ and we note that $h_i(y) = f_i g t_i(y)$. And $h(x, y)$ is clearly recursive. Hence for each number i such that $\omega_i \in \Sigma$, the function $h_i(y)$ is a productive function for $\tilde{\omega}_i$. Hence all the elements of Σ are uniformly creative (under $h(x, y)$).

THEOREM 8. If all elements of Σ are uniformly weakly creative then they are uniformly creative.

PROOF. Let $g(x, y)$ be such that for every $\omega_i \in \Sigma$, g_i is a weakly productive function for $\tilde{\omega}_i$. Let A be a fixed r.e. set.

By Theorem 4.6, Chapter IV there is a recursive function $t(x, y)$ such that for every i and j: $j \in A \longrightarrow t_i(j)$ index of $\{g_i t_i(j)\}$; $j \notin A \longrightarrow t_i(j)$ index of $\emptyset$.

Now let $\omega_i \in \Sigma$. Then we have:

(i) For every j, $j \in A \longrightarrow t_i(j)$ index of $\{g_i t_i(j)\}$;
$j \notin A \longrightarrow t_i(j)$ index of $\emptyset$.

(ii) $g_i(x)$ is weakly productive for $\tilde{\omega}_i$.

Then by Theorem 6, (b), $g_i t_i(x)$ is a reduction of A to ω_i. We then define $f(y, x) = g[y, t(y, x)]$ and note that $f_i(x) = g_i t_i(x)$.

So for every i such that $\omega_i \in \Sigma$, f_i is a reduction of A to ω_i. So f is a uniform reduction of A to all elements of Σ.

We have thus proved that if Σ is uniformly weakly creative, then for any r.e. set A, A is uniformly reducible to all elements of Σ. We now take A to be any creative set, and our theorem then follows from Theorem 7.

§8. UNIVERSAL SETS

A set γ is called universal iff every r.e. set is $1 - 1$ reducible to it, and uniformly universal iff all r.e. sets are uniformly $1 - 1$ reducible to it. An example (due to Post) of a r.e. set γ which is universal - in fact uniformly universal - is the following: Let $J(x, y)$ be a recursive pairing function; let γ be the set of all numbers $J(x, y)$ such that $y \in \omega_x$. Thus $y \in \omega_i \longleftrightarrow J(i, y) \in \gamma \longleftrightarrow J_i(y) \in \gamma$, so J_i is a $1 - 1$ reduction of ω_i to γ.

From the fact that there exists a r.e. set which is uniformly universal it is virtually immediate that every universal set is uniformly universal. For suppose α is a universal set. Let β be any r.e. set which is uniformly universal; let it be so under $f(x, y)$. Since β is r.e. then β is $1 - 1$ reducible to α; let $g(x)$ be a $1 - 1$ reduction of β to α. Then all r.e. sets are uniformly $1 - 1$ reducible to α under the function $g(f(x, y))$.

§9. ON UNIFORM REDUCIBILITY

Our next theorem is rather surprising, and has an interesting application to representation systems.

THEOREM 9. (a) If all recursive sets are uniformly reducible to γ then $\tilde{\gamma}$ is productive. Hence if all recursive sets are uniformly reducible to γ and γ is r.e. then γ is creative (and hence universal).

(b) A sufficient condition for $\tilde{\gamma}$ to be productive is that all finite sets -- or even all sets with at most one element -- be uniformly reducible to γ under a function $f(x, y)$ which is $1 - 1$ (i.e., such that for all x, x', y, y', $f(x, y) = f(x', y') \longrightarrow [x = x' \wedge y = y']$).

Before we prove Theorem 9 we shall establish a lemma which will have other applications as well.

Let Σ be an arbitrary collection of r.e. sets; let α be an arbitrary number set. Let us say that $\tilde{\alpha}$ is productive relative to Σ

if there is a recursive function $g(x)$ (under which $\tilde{\alpha}$ will be said to be productive relative to Σ) such that for every number i for which $\omega_i \in \Sigma$ and ω_i is disjoint from α, the number $g(i)$ is outside both α and ω_i. [We note that if $\tilde{\alpha}$ is productive relative to the collection of all sets with at most 1 element, then $\tilde{\alpha}$ is weakly productive. Hence, by Theorem 6 - Corollary 2, if $\tilde{\alpha}$ is productive relative to the collection of all recursive sets -- or even relative to the collection of all sets with at most one element -- then $\tilde{\alpha}$ is productive (i.e., productive relative to the collection of all r.e. sets).] We shall also say that $\tilde{\alpha}$ is <u>completely productive relative to</u> Σ if there is a recursive function $g(x)$ such that for every number i for which $\omega_i \in \Sigma$, the number $g(i)$ is either inside or outside both sets ω_i and α -- i.e., $g(i) \in \omega_i \longleftrightarrow g(i) \in \alpha$.

LEMMA A. Let the following conditions be satisfied:

(1) $f(x, y)$ is a uniform reduction of Σ to α.

(2) For any set A, if A is an element of Σ then so is the set A^* of all numbers x such that $f(x, x) \in A$.

Then $\tilde{\alpha}$ is completely productive relative to Σ.

PROOF. The set A^* is the inverse image of A under the diagonal function $\vec{f}$ of f. Hence the operation: $\Phi(A) = A^*$ is effective; let $t(x)$ be a recursive function such that for every i, $\omega_{t(i)} = \omega_i^*$. Now define $g(x)$ to be $f(t(x), t(x))$. [We note for future reference that the construction of $g(x)$ does not depend on the set α, but only on the function f.] We assert that $\tilde{\alpha}$ is completely productive relative to Σ under the function $g(x)$.

Let $\omega_i \in \Sigma$. Then so is ω_i^* -- i.e., so is $\omega_{t(i)}$. Then $f_{t(i)}$ is a reduction of ω_i^* to α -- i.e., for every x:

$$f(t(i), x) \in \alpha \longleftrightarrow x \in \omega_i^*$$

$$\longleftrightarrow f(x, x) \in \omega_i .$$

Setting $x = t(i)$ we have:

$$f(t(i), t(i)) \in \alpha \longleftrightarrow f(t(i), t(i)) \in \omega_i$$

i.e.,

$$g(i) \in \alpha \longleftrightarrow g(i) \in \omega_i ,$$

which was to be proved.

PROOF OF THEOREM 9.

(a) Suppose all recursive sets are uniformly reducible to γ under $f(x, y)$. For any set A, if A is recursive then so is A^*.

Thus the conditions of the preceeding lemma are fulfilled. Hence $\tilde{\gamma}$ is productive relative to the collection of recursive sets. Then $\tilde{\gamma}$ is productive, by Theorem 6 - Corollary 2.

(b) Proof same as (a), with the modification that if A contains at most one element, so does A^* (under the assumption that $f(x, y)$ is 1 - 1).

We remarked in the proof of Lemma A that the function $g(x)$ did not depend on the set α, but only on the function f. We thus can obtain the stronger theorem:

*THEOREM 9'. Let $t(x)$ and $f(x, y)$ be two recursive functions which are related by the following condition: For every number i, $\omega_{t(i)} = \overrightarrow{f}^{-1}(\omega_i)$ -- i.e., for every i and x, $x \in \omega_{t(i)} \longleftrightarrow f(x, x) \in \omega_i$).

Then $f[t(x, t(x)]$ has the following property:

For any set γ, if $f(x, y)$ uniformly reduces all recursive sets to γ -- or if $f(x, y)$ is 1 - 1 and uniformly reduces all sets with at most one element to γ -- then $f[t(x), t(x)]$ is a weakly productive function for γ.

§10. UNIFORM REPRESENTABILITY

We say that all elements of a collection Σ (of r.e. sets) are <u>uniformly representable</u> in a system Q iff there is a recursive function $t(x)$ such that for every number i for which $\omega_i \in \Sigma$, $t(i)$ is the Gödel number of some predicate of Q which represents ω_i in Q.

Theorem 9 now has the following application:

THEOREM 10.

(a) If all <u>recursive</u> sets are uniformly representable in Q and Q is formal, then Q is creative.

(b) If all sets with at most one element are uniformly representable in Q and Q is formal, and if the representation function Φ of Q is 1 - 1, then Q is creative.

PROOF. The hypothesis clearly implies that $\varphi(x, y)$ is a uniform reduction of all recursive sets to T_0 (since if H represents A in Q, φ_h is a reduction of A to T_0). Result is then immediate from Theorem 9.

§11. BI-UNIFORMITY

Let Σ_1, Σ_2 be two collections of r.e. sets. We shall say that the elements of Σ_1 are all reducible to all elements of Σ_2 in a bi-uniform manner, or that all elements of Σ_1 are bi-uniformly reducible to all elements of Σ_2 iff there is a recursive function $f(x, y, z)$ such that for all numbers i, j for which $\omega_j \in \Sigma_1$ and $\omega_i \in \Sigma_2$, $f_{i,j}$ is a reduction of ω_j to ω_i. [We recall the terminology: $f_{i,j}(x) = f(i, j, x)$. We also recall: $f_i(y, z) \underset{df}{=} f(i, y, z)$.] Such a function $f(x, y, z)$ shall be called a bi-uniform reduction of Σ_1 to Σ_2.

We note that the following conditions are equivalent:

(1) $f(x, y, z)$ is a bi-uniform reduction of Σ_1 to Σ_2.

(2) For each ω_i in Σ_2, f_i is a uniform reduction of Σ_1 to ω_i.

*THEOREM 11. A sufficient condition for all elements of Σ to be uniformly creative is that either:

(1) All recursive sets are bi-uniformly reducible to all elements of Σ.

(2) All sets with at most one element are bi-uniformly reducible to all elements of Σ under a function $f(x, y, z)$ such that for every number i, f_i is a $1 - 1$ function.

PROOF. Let $f(x, y, z)$ satisfy either (1) or (2). There is a recursive function $t(x, y)$ such that for every i, and j, $\omega_{t_i(j)} = (\vec{f}_i)^{-1}(\omega_j)$ [this follows readily from §4, Chapter IV]. Now let ω_i be any element in Σ. Then the following conditions hold:

(1) f_i is a uniform reduction of all recursive sets to ω_i, or f_i is $1 - 1$ and is a uniform reduction of all sets with at most one element to ω_i.

(2) For every i, $\omega_{t_i(j)} = (\vec{f}_i)^{-1}(\omega_j)$.

Then by Theorem 9', the function $f_i[t_i(x), t_i(x)]$ is weakly productive for ω_i. We thus define $g(x, y) \underset{df}{=} f_x[t_x(y), t_x(y)]$, and for every $\omega_i \in \Sigma$, g_i is weakly productive for ω_i. Therefore all elements of Σ are uniformly weakly creative, hence they are uniformly creative by Theorem 8.

#C. EFFECTIVE INSEPARABILITY AND DOUBLE PRODUCTIVITY

§12. DOUBLY PRODUCTIVE PAIRS

For two number sets α and β, we shall say that the pair (α, β) is <u>doubly productive</u> iff there is a recursive function $k(x, y)$ (under which (α, β) is said to be double productive) such that for any two respective subsets ω_i, ω_j of $(\alpha \cup \tilde{\beta})$, $(\beta \cup \tilde{\alpha})$ which are disjoint from each other, $k(i, j) \in (\alpha \cap \beta) - (\omega_i \cup \omega_j)$.[1]

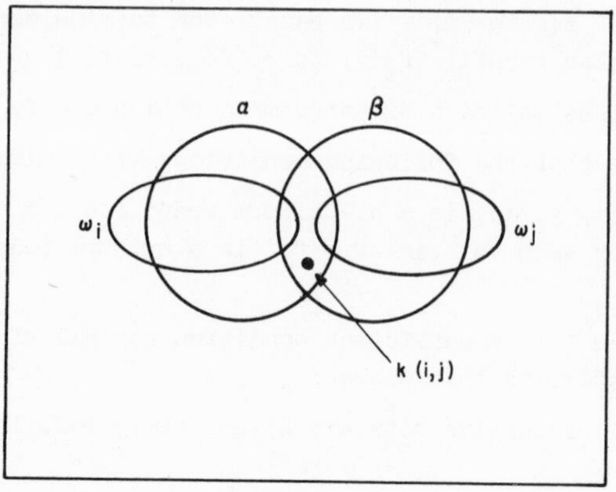

FIGURE 5

We note that the pair $(\tilde{\alpha}, \tilde{\beta})$ is doubly productive under $k(x, y)$ iff for every two numbers i, j such that ω_i, ω_j are disjoint and such that ω_i, ω_j are respectively disjoint from $\alpha - \beta$, $\beta - \alpha$, the number $k(i, j)$ is outside all four sets $\alpha, \beta, \omega_i, \omega_j$.

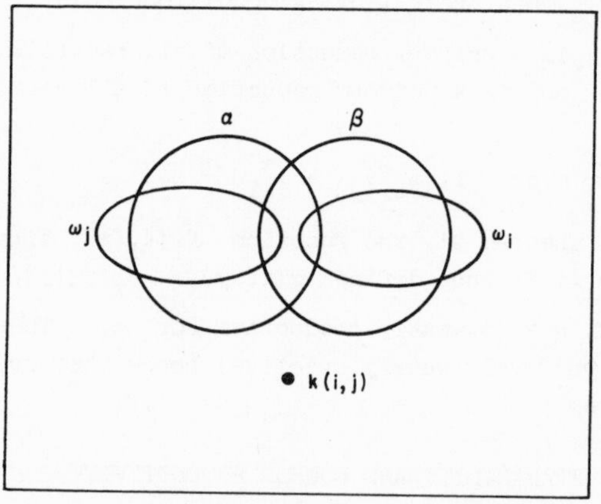

FIGURE 6

---

1 Our definition of double productivity differs from the one given in the first edition of this monograph, though the one given there is correct for disjoint pairs. For the observation that the original definition was inadequate for intersecting pairs, we are indebted to T. G. McLaughlin.

It is obviously impossible for a disjoint pair (α, β) to be doubly productive. We shall usually be interested in pairs (α, β) such that the pair $(\tilde{\alpha}, \tilde{\beta})$ is doubly productive. For a disjoint pair (α, β), the pair $(\tilde{\alpha}, \tilde{\beta})$ is doubly productive under $k(x, y)$ iff for every i, j for which ω_i, ω_j are disjoint and respectively disjoint from α, β, the number $k(i, j)$ is outside all four sets α, β, ω_i, ω_j.

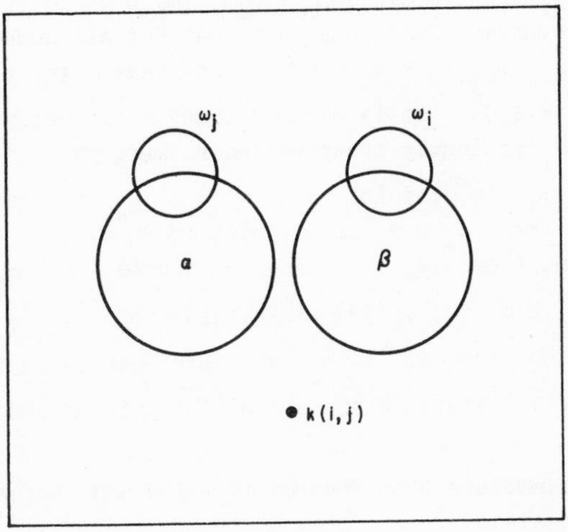

FIGURE 7

We call a pair (α, β) doubly creative iff α, β are both r.e. and $(\tilde{\alpha}, \tilde{\beta})$ is doubly productive. If $(\tilde{\alpha}, \tilde{\beta})$ is doubly productive under $k(x, y)$, and if α, β are both r.e., then we shall sometimes say that (α, β) is doubly creative under $k(x, y)$.

It is obvious that (α, β) is a doubly productive pair iff (β, α) is a doubly productive pair.

THEOREM 12. Let α, β be disjoint. Then

(a) If $(\tilde{\alpha}, \tilde{\beta})$ is doubly productive, (α, β) is E.I.

(b) If (α, β) is E.I. and if α, β are both r.e. then $(\tilde{\alpha}, \tilde{\beta})$ is doubly productive -- i.e., (α, β) is doubly creative.

Thus a necessary and sufficient condition for a disjoint pair (α, β) of r.e. sets to be E.I. is that it be doubly creative.

PROOF. (a) This part is trivial. Suppose $(\tilde{\alpha}, \tilde{\beta})$ is doubly productive. Then $(\tilde{\beta}, \tilde{\alpha})$ is doubly productive; let it be doubly productive under $k(x, y)$. Then $k(x, y)$ must be an E.I. function for

(α, β). For suppose $\alpha \subseteq \omega_i$; $\beta \subseteq \omega_j$; ω_i is disjoint from ω_j. Then ω_i is disjoint from β, ω_j is disjoint from α, so $k(i, j)$ is outside all four sets $\alpha, \beta, \omega_i, \omega_j$. Then $k(i, j)$ is certainly outside ω_i and ω_j. Hence $k(x, y)$ is an E.I. function for (α, β).

(b) Suppose (α, β) is E.I.; let $\delta(x, y)$ be an E.I. function for (β, α). Since β is r.e. then the operation $\Phi(\omega_i) = \omega_i \cup \beta$ is effective; likewise the operation $\Phi(\omega_i) = \omega_i \cup \alpha$ is effective. Let $\varphi_1(x), \varphi_2(x)$ be recursive functions such that for all numbers i, $\omega_{\varphi_1(i)} = \omega_i \cup \beta$ and $\omega_{\varphi_2(i)} = \omega_i \cup \alpha$. We now take $k(x, y)$ to be the function $\delta[\varphi_1(x), \varphi_2(y)]$. It is obvious that k is recursive, and we assert that (α, β) is doubly creative under $k(x, y)$.

Suppose ω_i is disjoint from α and ω_j is disjoint from both ω_i and β. Then $\omega_i \cup \beta$ is disjoint from $\omega_j \cup \alpha$ -- i.e., $\omega_{\varphi_1(i)}$ is disjoint from $\omega_{\varphi_2(j)}$. And, of course, $\beta \subseteq \omega_{\varphi_1(i)}$; $\alpha \subseteq \omega_{\varphi_2(j)}$. Hence $\delta(\varphi_1(i), \varphi_2(j))$ is outside both $\omega_{\varphi_1(i)}$ and $\omega_{\varphi_2(j)}$ i.e., $k(i, j)$ is outside $\omega_i, \beta, \omega_j, \alpha$, which was to be proved.

COROLLARY 1. There exists a disjoint pair of doubly creative sets.

PROOF. Immediate from Theorem 12 - (b) and the existence of an E.I. pair of r.e. sets.

THEOREM 13. Let α, β be disjoint and r.e. Let Σ_α be the collection of all r.e. supersets of α which are disjoint from β. Then a necessary and sufficient condition for (α, β) to be E.I. is that all elements of Σ_α are uniformly creative.

PROOF. (a) Suppose (α, β) is E.I. Then (β, α) is E.I. hence (β, α) is doubly creative by Theorem 12; let $k(x, y)$ be a recursive function under which it is doubly creative. Let ω_i be any r.e. superset of α disjoint from β; we show that $k_i(y)$ is a productive function for $\tilde{\omega}_i$. Let ω_j be any r.e. set disjoint from ω_i. Then (i) (ω_i, ω_j) are disjoint; (ii) ω_i is disjoint from β; (iii) ω_j is disjoint from α. Then $k(i, j) \notin (\alpha \cup \beta \cup \omega_i \cup \omega_j)$. Hence $k(i, j) \notin \omega_i \cup \omega_j$ -- i.e., $k_i(j) \notin (\omega_i \cup \omega_j)$. So k_i is productive for $\tilde{\omega}_i$. This proves that all elements of Σ_α are uniformly creative.

(b) Suppose all elements of Σ_α are uniformly creative; let $g(x, y)$ be witness to the fact. Then it is obvious that $g(x, y)$ is an E.I. function for (α, β). For suppose (ω_i, ω_j) are disjoint supersets of (α, β). Then $\omega_i \in \Sigma_\alpha$, so $g_i(y)$ is productive for $\tilde{\omega}_i$. Then $g_i(j) \notin \omega_i \cup \omega_j$ -- i.e., $g(i, j) \notin \omega_i \cup \omega_j$.

REMARK. The proof of (b) is valid without the assumption that either α or β is r.e.

COROLLARY 1. If all r.e. supersets of α disjoint from β are uniformly weakly creative, and if α, β are disjoint, then (α, β) is E.I.

PROOF. By Theorem 8 and Theorem 13.

*COROLLARY 2. A sufficient condition for a disjoint pair (α, β) to be E.I. is that all recursive sets are bi-uniformly reducible to all r.e. supersets of α disjoint from β.

PROOF. By Theorem 11 and Theorem 13.

DISCUSSION. It follows at once from Theorem 13 that if (γ_1, γ_2) are E.I. and r.e. then they are each creative (this fact is well known, and can be established by a more direct argument). However if (γ_1, γ_2) are disjoint creative sets, they are not necessarily E.I. To see a simple counter example, take two infinite disjoint r.e. sets α and β. By a well know theorem of Post, α and β respectively contain infinite recursive subsets α' and β'; those in turn respectively contain creative subsets α'' and β''. These latter are recursively separated by α', β', so they are not even R.I., let alone E.I.

§13. REDUCIBILITY OF PAIRS TO PAIRS

For most of the remaining results of this chapter we must generalize the notions of many-one and 1 - 1 reducibility of sets to sets to that of pairs of sets to pairs of sets.

Let (A_1, A_2), (B_1, B_2) each be an ordered pair of number sets. Let $f(x)$ be a recursive function. We say that f reduces the pair (A_1, A_2) to (B_1, B_2), or that f is a reduction of the first pair to the second iff $A_1 = f^{-1}(B_1)$ and $A_2 = f^{-1}(B_2)$. Thus f reduces (A_1, A_2) to (B_1, B_2) iff f simultaneously reduces A_1 to B_1 and A_2 to B_2. Thus a reduction of (A_1, A_2) to (B_1, B_2) is a recursive function which maps A_1 into B_1, A_2 into B_2 and the complement of $A_1 \cup A_2$ into the complement of $B_1 \cup B_2$. Equivalently, f is a reduction of (A_1, A_2) to (B_1, B_2) iff the following conditions hold for every number x:

(1) $x \in A_1 \longleftrightarrow f(x) \in B_1$

(2) $x \in A_2 \longleftrightarrow f(x) \in B_2$.

We say that (A_1, A_2) is reducible to (B_1, B_2) iff there is a recursive function f which reduces (A_1, A_2) to (B_1, B_2). If there is a 1 - 1 recursive function f which reduces (A_1, A_2) to (B_1, B_2)

then we say that (A_1, A_2) is $1 - 1$ reducible to (B_1, B_2), also that such a function $f(x)$ is a $1 - 1$ reduction of (A_1, A_2) to (B_1, B_2).

If f is a reduction of (A_1, A_2) to (B_1, B_2) then f obviously recursively maps (A_1, A_2) into (B_1, B_2); the converse is not necessarily true.

The following proposition and theorem will have applications in Section D.

PROPOSITION 7. If (A_1, A_2) is reducible to (B_1, B_2) and if $(\tilde{A}_1, \tilde{A}_2)$ is doubly productive then $(\tilde{B}_1, \tilde{B}_2)$ is doubly productive.

PROOF. Let $(\tilde{A}_1, \tilde{A}_2)$ be doubly productive under $k(x, y)$; let f be a reduction of (A_1, A_2) to (B_1, B_2). Let $t(x)$ be a recursive function such that for every number i, $\omega_{t(i)} = f^{-1}(\omega_i)$. Define $k'(x, y) = f[k(t(x), t(y))]$. We assert that $(\tilde{B}_1, \tilde{B}_2)$ is doubly productive under k'.

Suppose ω_i, ω_j obey the conditions.

(1) ω_i, ω_j are disjoint
(2) ω_i is disjoint from $B_1 - B_2$
(3) ω_j is disjoint from $B_2 - B_1$

We must show that $k'(i, j)$ is outside all four sets $B_1, B_2, \omega_i, \omega_j$. By (1), $f^{-1}(\omega_i)$ is disjoint from $f^{-1}(\omega_j)$ — i.e., $\omega_{t(i)}$ is disjoint from $\omega_{t(j)}$. By (2), $f^{-1}(\omega_i)$ is disjoint from $f^{-1}(B_1 - B_2)$ — i.e., $\omega_{t(i)}$ is disjoint from $A_1 - A_2$. By (3), $f^{-1}(\omega_j)$ is disjoint from $f^{-1}(B_2 - B_1)$ — i.e., $\omega_{t(j)}$ is disjoint from $A_2 - A_1$. Then, since $(\tilde{A}_1, \tilde{A}_2)$ is doubly productive under k, $k(t(i), t(j))$ is outside all four sets $A_1, A_2, \omega_{t(i)}, \omega_{t(j)}$. Hence $fk(t(i), t(j))$ is outside all four sets $B_1, B_2, \omega_i, \omega_j$, which was to be proved.

THEOREM 14. If every disjoint pair of r.e. sets is many-one reducible to (α, β) then $(\tilde{\alpha}, \tilde{\beta})$ is doubly productive.

PROOF. By Theorem 12, Corollary 1 there exists a pair (γ_1, γ_2) of disjoint r.e. sets such that $(\tilde{\gamma}_1, \tilde{\gamma}_2)$ is doubly productive. By hypothesis (γ_1, γ_2) is reducible to (α, β). Then $(\tilde{\gamma}_1, \tilde{\gamma}_2)$ is reducible to $(\tilde{\alpha}, \tilde{\beta})$. Hence $(\tilde{\alpha}, \tilde{\beta})$ is doubly productive, by Proposition 7.

§14. DOUBLY UNIVERSAL AND TOTALLY DOUBLY UNIVERSAL PAIRS

A pair (γ_1, γ_2) of number sets is called doubly universal (abbreviated D.U.) iff every disjoint pair of r.e. sets is 1 - 1 reducible to it (cf. §13). We shall call (γ_1, γ_2) totally D.U. (also abbreviated D.U.$^+$) iff every pair of r.e. sets (whether disjoint or not) is 1 - 1 reducible to (γ_1, γ_2).

We note that it is impossible for a disjoint pair (γ_1, γ_2) to be totally D.U. For suppose (γ_1, γ_2) is totally D.U. Take any pair (α, β) of r.e. sets which have a non-empty intersection. Then $(\alpha, \beta) \underset{f}{\rightarrow} (\gamma_1, \gamma_2)$ for some recursive function f. Then clearly f maps $\alpha \cap \beta$ into $\gamma_1 \cap \gamma_2$, so $\gamma_1 \cap \gamma_2$ cannot be empty.

We also note that if (γ_1, γ_2) is D.U.$^+$ -- or even D.U. -- or even if every disjoint pair of r.e. sets is many-one reducible to (γ_1, γ_2), then $\tilde{\gamma}_1, \tilde{\gamma}_2$ are both productive sets. For we can take some disjoint pair (α, β) of creative sets (e.g., an E.I. pair); this pair is then reducible to (γ_1, γ_2), hence α is reducible to γ_1 and β is reducible to γ_2. Then $\tilde{\gamma}_1$ and $\tilde{\gamma}_2$ must be productive.

§15. UNIFORM REDUCIBILITY

Let Σ be a collection of ordered pairs of r.e. sets; let f(x, y, z) be a recursive function. We say that all elements of Σ are uniformly reducible to (γ_1, γ_2) under f iff the following condition holds: For every pair of numbers i, j for which $(\omega_i, \omega_j) \in \Sigma$, $f_{i,j}$ reduces (ω_i, ω_j) to (γ_1, γ_2). If there is such a recursive function f, then we say that all elements of Σ are uniformly reducible to (γ_1, γ_2); If furthermore for each i, j, $f_{i,j}(z)$ is a 1 - 1 function, then we say that all elements of Σ are uniformly 1 - 1 reducible to (γ_1, γ_2). The pair (γ_1, γ_2) is called uniformly doubly universal iff all disjoint pairs (ω_i, ω_j) are uniformly 1 - 1 reducible to (γ_1, γ_2). And we call (γ_1, γ_2) uniformly D.U.$^+$ iff all pairs of r.e. sets are uniformly 1 - 1 reducible to (γ_1, γ_2).

An example of a pair (U_1, U_2) of r.e. sets which is D.U.$^+$ -- in fact uniformly so -- is the following: Let f(x, y, z) be any recursive 1 - 1 function. Define U_1 to be the set of all numbers of the form f(x, y, z) such that $z \in \omega_x$; define U_2 to be the set of all numbers of the form f(x, y, z) such that $z \in \omega_y$. Then clearly for any r.e. sets ω_i, ω_j, $f_{i,j}(z) \in U_1 \longleftrightarrow z \in \omega_i$, and $f_{i,j}(z) \in U_2 \longleftrightarrow z \in \omega_j$. Thus $f_{i,j}$ is a 1 - 1 reduction of (ω_i, ω_j) to (U_1, U_2).

An example of a disjoint pair (U_1', U_2') of r.e. sets which is uniformly doubly universal is the following. Take $f(x, y, z)$ as before. Let U_1' be the set of all numbers $f(x, y, z)$ such that $z \in \omega_x$ before $z \in \omega_y$; let U_2' be the set of all numbers $f(x, y, z)$ such that $z \in \omega_y$ before $z \in \omega_x$. (cf. §13, Chapter IV). It is easily verified that for any sets (ω_i, ω_j) which are disjoint, $f_{i,j}$ is a 1 - 1 reduction of (ω_i, ω_j) to (U_1', U_2'). And it is obvious that U_1', U_2' are r.e. and disjoint.

It is obvious that if $f(x, y, z)$ is a uniform reduction of Σ to (γ_1, γ_2) and if h is a reduction of (γ_1, γ_2) to (α, β) then $hf(x, y, z)$ is a uniform reduction of Σ to (α, β). Also if $f(x, y, z)$ is a uniform 1 - 1 reduction of Σ to (γ_1, γ_2) and if h is a 1 - 1 reduction of (γ_1, γ_2) to (α, β) then $hf(x, y, z)$ is a uniform 1 - 1 reduction to Σ to (α, β). And since there exists a uniformly D.U.$^+$ pair of r.e. sets and there exists a uniformly doubly universal pair of disjoint r.e. sets we can assert:

(1) If all pairs of r.e. sets are reducible to (α, β) then all pairs are uniformly reducible to (α, β).

(2) If (α, β) is D.U.$^+$ it is uniformly so.

(3) If all disjoint pairs of r.e. sets are reducible to (α, β) then all such pairs are uniformly reducible to (α, β).

(4) If (α, β) is doubly universal then it is uniformly so.

We shall subsequently show that if all disjoint pairs of <u>recursive</u> sets are uniformly reducible to (γ_1, γ_2) then the latter pair is doubly universal.

Let (σ_1, σ_2) be any pair of E.I. sets which are r.e. Then (σ_1, σ_2) is reducible to (γ_1, γ_2), so (γ_1, γ_2) is E.I. by Proposition 4, Corollary 1. Thus any disjoint pair of doubly universal sets is E.I. We now aim to show that every E.I. pair of r.e. sets is doubly universal. [This is the "double" analogue of Myhill's theorem that every creative set is universal.]

§16. WEAKLY DOUBLY PRODUCTIVE PAIRS

We now wish to use recursive pairing functions $J(x, y)$, $K(x)$, $L(x)$ such that $J(x, y)$ is <u>onto</u> N (i.e., such that every number z is of the form $J(x, y)$). So the functions J, K, L of Chapter IV will no longer suffice. However we no longer need our recursive pairing functions to be rudimentary, so we can take $J(x, y)$ to be the standard function: $\frac{1}{2}(x + y - 1)(x + y - 2) + y$. Then for every x, $K(x)$ and $L(x)$ are defined and $J(K(x), L(x)) = x$.

It is obvious that $(\tilde{\alpha}, \tilde{\beta})$ is doubly productive iff there is a recursive function $g(x)$ [under which $(\tilde{\alpha}, \tilde{\beta})$ will again be said to be doubly productive] such that for every number i such that ω_{Ki}, ω_{Li} are disjoint from each other and respectively disjoint from $(\alpha - \beta)$, $(\beta - \alpha)$, g(i) is outside all four sets α, β, ω_{Ki}, ω_{Li}. For if $(\tilde{\alpha}, \tilde{\beta})$ is doubly productive under the function k(x, y) of two arguments, then the pair is doubly productive under a function g(x); viz. k[Kx, Lx]. And if $(\tilde{\alpha}, \tilde{\beta})$ is doubly productive under a function g(x) of one argument, then it is doubly productive under k(x, y); viz. g [J(x, y)].

We shall now define $(\tilde{\alpha}, \tilde{\beta})$ to be weakly doubly productive iff there is a recursive function g(x) [under which $(\tilde{\alpha}, \tilde{\beta})$ will be said to be weakly doubly productive] such that for any number i such that ω_{Ki}, ω_{Li} are disjoint sets with at most one element between them (i.e., they are either both empty or else one of them is empty and the other one is a unit set), the following conditions hold:

(1) If ω_{Ki} is a unit set disjoint from α, then $g(i) \notin \omega_{Ki}$.
(2) If ω_{Li} is a unit set disjoint from β, then $g(i) \notin \omega_{Li}$.
(3) If ω_{Ki}, ω_{Li} are both empty then $g(i) \notin \alpha \cup \beta$.

It is obvious that if (α, β) is doubly productive then it is weakly doubly productive. We shall soon prove the converse.

§17. ON DOUBLY PRODUCTIVE PAIRS

Myhill [14] showed that if α is creative then there exists a monotone strictly increasing productive function for $\tilde{\alpha}$. We now need the "double" analogue of this fact.

PROPOSITION 8. If $(\tilde{\alpha}, \tilde{\beta})$ is doubly productive then it is doubly productive under a monotone strictly increasing function $g^*(x)$.

PROOF. Let $(\tilde{\alpha}, \tilde{\beta})$ be doubly productive under g(x). It is easily verified that there is a recursive function $h_1(x)$ such that for all x, $\omega_{h_1(x)} = \omega_{Lx} \cup \{g(x)\}$. Let $h(x) = J[K(x), h_1(x)]$. Then $Khx = Kx$; $Lhx = h_1(x)$. Thus $\{\omega_{Khx}, \omega_{Lhx}\} = \{\omega_{Kx}, (\omega_{Lx} \cup \{g(x)\})\}$.

We let σ be the set of all numbers i such that ω_{Ki}, ω_{Li} are disjoint from each other and respectively disjoint from $\alpha - \beta$, $\beta - \alpha$.

We now consider the sequence g(i), gh(i), ghh(i), ghhh(i), ... It follows from the definition of h(x) that if $i \in \sigma$ then all terms of the above sequence are distinct and outside all four sets, α, β, ω_{Ki}, ω_{Li}. We define the function $g^*(x)$ by induction: Let $g^*(1) = g(1)$. Suppose $g^*(n)$ has been defined. Then define $g^*(n+1)$ as follows: Generate the above sequence until either a repetition occurs (in which case $(n+1) \notin \sigma$) or a number m is reached which exceeds $g^*(n)$.

In the former case, set $g^*(n+1) = 1 + g^*(n)$ (so that $g^*(n+1) > g^*(n)$). In the latter case set $g^*(n+1) = m$. Then $g^*(x)$ is strictly monotone increasing (and hence is 1 - 1) and is a doubly productive function for $(\tilde{\alpha}, \tilde{\beta})$.

COROLLARY 1. If (α, β) is doubly productive then it is weakly doubly productive under a 1 - 1 function $g(x)$.

Our next theorem underlies several of our main results.

THEOREM 15.

(1) If $(\tilde{\gamma}_1, \tilde{\gamma}_2)$ is weakly doubly productive then every disjoint pair of r.e. sets is many-one reducible to (γ_1, γ_2).

(2) If $(\tilde{\gamma}_1, \tilde{\gamma}_2)$ is weakly doubly productive under a 1 - 1 function $g(x)$ then (γ_1, γ_2) is double universal.

PROOF. (1) Let $(\tilde{\gamma}_1, \tilde{\gamma}_2)$ be weakly doubly productive under $g(x)$. Let (α, β) be any pair of disjoint r.e. sets. By Theorem 5.1, Chapter IV there is a 1 - 1 recursive function $t(x)$ such that for every number i the following conditions hold:

(1) $i \in \alpha \longrightarrow \omega_{Kt(i)} = \{gt(i)\}$
(2) $i \notin \alpha \longrightarrow \omega_{Kt(i)} = \emptyset$
(3) $i \in \beta \longrightarrow \omega_{Lt(i)} = \{gt(i)\}$
(4) $i \notin \beta \longrightarrow \omega_{Lt(i)} = \emptyset$.

We thus have:

(a) $i \in \alpha \longrightarrow \{\omega_{Kt(i)}, \omega_{Lt(i)}\} = \{\{gt(i), \emptyset\}$
(b) $i \in \beta \longrightarrow \{\omega_{Kt(i)}, \omega_{Lt(i)}\} = \{\emptyset, \{gt(i)\}\}$
(c) $i \notin (\alpha \cup \beta) \longrightarrow \{\omega_{Kt(i)}, \omega_{Lt(i)}\} = \{\emptyset, \emptyset\}$.

We note that in all cases (a), (b), (c), $\omega_{Kt(i)}, \omega_{Lt(i)}$ are disjoint r.e. sets with at most one element between them.

We now show that $gt(x)$ is a reduction of (α, β) to (γ_1, γ_2).

(a) Suppose $i \in \alpha$. Then $\omega_{Kt(i)} = \{gt(i)\}$, so $gt(i) \in \omega_{Kti}$. If ω_{Kti} were disjoint from $\gamma_1 - \gamma_2$ then $gt(i)$ would be outside ω_{Kti} (since $(\tilde{\gamma}_1, \tilde{\gamma}_2)$ is weakly doubly productive under $g(x)$). Therefore ω_{Kti} intersects $(\gamma_1 - \gamma_2)$— i.e., $\{gt(i)\}$ intersects $(\gamma_1 - \gamma_2)$, so $gt(i) \in (\gamma_1 - \gamma_2)$. We have thus shown: $i \in \alpha \longrightarrow gt(i) \in (\gamma_1 - \gamma_2)$.

(b) By symmetric reasoning, $i \in \beta \longrightarrow gt(i) \in (\gamma_2 - \gamma_1)$

(c) Suppose $i \notin \alpha \cup \beta$. Then $\omega_{Kt(i)}, \omega_{Lt(i)}$ are both empty, so $gt(i) \notin \gamma_1 \cup \gamma_2$.

So by (a), (b), (c), $gt(x)$ is a reduction of (α, β) to (γ_1, γ_2). This proves (1).

(2) If g is 1 - 1 so is $gt(x)$ (since t is 1 - 1).

THEOREM 16. If $(\tilde{\gamma}_1, \tilde{\gamma}_2)$ is doubly productive then (γ_1, γ_2) is doubly universal.

PROOF. Suppose $(\tilde{\gamma}_1, \tilde{\gamma}_2)$ is doubly productive. Then by Proposition 8, Corollary 1, $(\tilde{\gamma}_1, \tilde{\gamma}_2)$ is weakly doubly productive under a $1-1$ function $g(x)$. Then (γ_1, γ_2) is D.U. by Theorem 15.

THEOREM 17. If every disjoint pair of r.e. sets is many-one reducible to (γ_1, γ_2) then (γ_1, γ_2) is doubly universal.

PROOF. Suppose that every disjoint pair of r.e. sets is many-one reducible to (γ_1, γ_2). Then by Theorem 14, $(\tilde{\gamma}_1, \tilde{\gamma}_2)$ is doubly productive. Then (γ_1, γ_2) is D.U. by Theorem 16.

From Theorem 17 we now obtain the following strengthening of Theorem 15, (1).

THEOREM 18. If $(\tilde{\gamma}_1, \tilde{\gamma}_2)$ is weakly doubly productive then (γ_1, γ_2) is doubly universal.

PROOF. Suppose $(\tilde{\gamma}_1, \tilde{\gamma}_2)$ is weakly doubly productive. Then by Theorem 15, (1), every disjoint pair of r.e. sets is many-one reducible to (γ_1, γ_2). Then (γ_1, γ_2) is doubly universal by Theorem 17.

A SUMMARY. We see, by Theorems 15-18 and Proposition 8 that the following conditions are all equivalent:

(i) $(\tilde{\gamma}_1, \tilde{\gamma}_2)$ is doubly productive.
(ii) $(\tilde{\gamma}_1, \tilde{\gamma}_2)$ is doubly productive under a $1-1$ function.
(iii) $(\tilde{\gamma}_1, \tilde{\gamma}_2)$ is weakly doubly productive.
(iv) $(\tilde{\gamma}_1, \tilde{\gamma}_2)$ is weakly doubly productive under a $1-1$ function.
(v) Every disjoint pair of r.e. sets is many-one reducible to (γ_1, γ_2).
(vi) (γ_1, γ_2) is doubly universal.

REMARK. If (γ_1, γ_2) is doubly productive then γ_1, γ_2 must be individually productive. For if (γ_1, γ_2) is doubly productive then $(\tilde{\gamma}_1, \tilde{\gamma}_2)$ is D.U., so γ_1, γ_2 are each productive (cf. last paragraph of §14).

THEOREM 19. Every E.I. pair of r.e. sets is doubly universal. Hence a disjoint pair of r.e. sets is E.I. iff it is D.U.[1]

---

[1] This is a "double" analogue of Myhill's theorem that every creative set is universal. It was first proved by Muchnik [13] and independently by Smullyan [30].

PROOF. Suppose (γ_1, γ_2) is an E.I. pair of r.e. sets. Then $(\tilde{\gamma}_1, \tilde{\gamma}_2)$ is doubly productive by Theorem 12. Hence (γ_1, γ_2) is D.U. by Theorem 16.

THEOREM 20. Let (γ_1, γ_2) be a D.U. pair of disjoint sets. Then every disjoint pair of r.e. supersets of γ_1, γ_2 is in turn D.U.

PROOF. Suppose that γ_1', γ_2' are disjoint r.e. supersets of γ_1, γ_2. Since (γ_1, γ_2) is D.U. then (γ_1, γ_2) is E.I. Hence (γ_1', γ_2') is E.I. Then (γ_1', γ_2') is D.U. by Theorem 19.

§18. APPLICATION TO ROSSER SYSTEMS

THEOREM 21. If Z is a consistent formal Rosser system then (T_o, R_o) is doubly universal.

PROOF. Let Z be a consistent Rosser system. Then (T_o, R_o) is E.I. by Theorem 4. If also Z is formal, then T_o and R_o are r.e. Then (T_o, R_o) is D.U. by Theorem 19.

§19. UNIFORM REDUCIBILITY

Let Σ be a collection of ordered pairs of r.e. sets; let (γ_1, γ_2) be a fixed pair of r.e. sets. In §15 we defined what it means for a recursive function $f(x, y, z)$ to be a uniform reduction of Σ to (γ_1, γ_2). An alternative characterization of uniform reducibility can be given using a function $g(x, y)$ of only two arguments. We shall say that $g(x, y)$ is a uniform reduction of Σ (or of all elements of Σ) to (γ_1, γ_2) iff $g(x, y)$ is recursive and for every number i such that $(\omega_{Ki}, \omega_{Li}) \in \Sigma$, g_i reduces $(\omega_{Ki}, \omega_{Li})$ to (γ_1, γ_2). If $f(x, y, z)$ is a uniform reduction of Σ to (γ_1, γ_2), then the function $g(x, y)$; viz., $f(Kx, Lx, y)$ is a uniform reduction of Σ to (γ_1, γ_2). And if $g(x, y)$ is a function which is a uniform reduction of Σ to (γ_1, γ_2) then the function $f(x, y, z)$; viz., $g[J(x, y), z]$, is a uniform reduction of Σ to (γ_1, γ_2).

We shall say that $(\tilde{\alpha}, \tilde{\beta})$ is <u>completely doubly productive relative to</u> Σ iff there is a recursive function $g(x)$ such that for every number i for which $(\omega_{Ki}, \omega_{Li}) \in \Sigma$, the following conditions both hold:

(1) $g(i) \in \alpha \longleftrightarrow g(i) \in \omega_{Ki}$.

(2) $g(i) \in \beta \longleftrightarrow g(i) \in \omega_{Li}$.

Alternatively, $(\tilde{\alpha}, \tilde{\beta})$ is completely doubly productive relative to Σ iff there is a recursive function $k(x, y)$ such that for any numbers i, j for which $(\omega_i, \omega_j) \in \Sigma$, the following conditions hold:

(1) $k(i, j) \in \alpha \longleftrightarrow k(i, j) \in \omega_i$.

(2) $k(i, j) \in \beta \longleftrightarrow k(i, j) \in \omega_j$.

The following lemma is a "double" analogue of Lemma A. In this lemma $f(x, y)$ is to be a fixed recursive function and for any number set A, A^* is to be the set of all numbers i such that $f_i(i) \in A$ -- i.e., such that $f(i, i) \in A$.

LEMMA B. If $f(x, y)$ is a uniform reduction of Σ to (γ_1, γ_2) and if for every pair $(A, B) \in \Sigma$ the pair (A^*, B^*) is also in Σ, then $(\tilde{\gamma}_1, \tilde{\gamma}_2)$ is completely doubly productive relative to Σ.

PROOF. As in the proof of Lemma A, there is a recursive function $t(x)$ such that for every number i, $\omega_{t(i)} = \omega_i^*$. Let $h(x) = J[tK(x), tL(x)]$. Then $h(x)$ is recursive and $Kh(x) = tK(x)$; $Lh(x) = tL(x)$. Thus

$$\omega_{Kh(i)} = \omega_{tK(i)} = \omega_{K(i)}^*$$

$$\omega_{Lh(i)} = \omega_{tL(i)} = \omega_{L(i)}^* .$$

We now define $g(x) \underset{df}{=} f[h(x), h(x)]$. The function $g(x)$ is recursive, and we show that it satisfies conditions (1) and (2).

Suppose $(\omega_{Ki}, \omega_{Li}) \in \Sigma$. Then by hypothesis $(\omega_{Ki}^*, \omega_{Li}^*) \in \Sigma$ -- i.e., $(\omega_{Kh(i)}, \omega_{Lh(i)}) \in \Sigma$. Since f is a uniform reduction of Σ to (γ_1, γ_2), $f_{h(i)}$ is then a reduction of $(\omega_{Kh(i)}, \omega_{Lh(i)})$ to (γ_1, γ_2). Hence for every number x we have:

$$\text{(a)}\quad f_{h(i)}(x) \in \gamma_1 \longleftrightarrow x \in \omega_{Kh(i)} \longleftrightarrow x \in \omega_{K(i)}^* \longleftrightarrow f_x(x) \in \omega_{K(i)}$$

$$\text{(b)}\quad f_{h(i)}(x) \in \gamma_2 \longleftrightarrow x \in \omega_{Lh(i)} \longleftrightarrow x \in \omega_{L(i)}^* \longleftrightarrow f_x(x) \in \omega_{L(i)} .$$

Setting $x = h(i)$ we have:

(a) $f_{h(i)}(h(i)) \in \gamma_1 \longleftrightarrow f_{h(i)}(h(i)) \in \omega_{K(i)}$ -- i.e.,

$$g(i) \in \gamma_1 \longleftrightarrow g(i) \in \omega_{K(i)}$$

(b) $f_{h(i)}(h(i)) \in \gamma_2 \longleftrightarrow f_{h(i)}(h(i)) \in \omega_{L(i)}$ -- i.e.,

$$g(i) \in \gamma_2 \longleftrightarrow g(i) \in \omega_{L(i)} .$$

THEOREM 22. [A "double" analogue of Theorem 9.]

(a) If all disjoint pairs of recursive sets are uniformly reducible to (γ_1, γ_2), then (γ_1, γ_2) is doubly universal.

(b) If all disjoint pairs of sets with at most one element between them are uniformly reducible to (γ_1, γ_2) under a $1 - 1$ function

$f(x, y)$ then (γ_1, γ_2) is again doubly universal.

PROOF. (a) Let Σ be the collection of all disjoint pairs of recursive sets. All elements of Σ are uniformly reducible to (γ_1, γ_2) by hypothesis. And if A is recursive, A^* is recursive; if (A, B) are disjoint (A^*, B^*) are disjoint. Hence if $(A, B) \in \Sigma$ then $(A^*, B^*) \in \Sigma$. Then they hypothesis of Lemma B is fulfilled. Hence $(\tilde{\gamma}_1, \tilde{\gamma}_2)$ is completely productive relative to Σ. Then $(\tilde{\gamma}_1, \tilde{\gamma}_2)$ is of course weakly doubly productive. Hence (γ_1, γ_2) is D.U. by Theorem 16.

(b) The proof is like (a), except that we let Σ be the collection of all disjoint pairs with at most one element between them, and note that if (A, B) is such a pair, then (A^*, B^*) is such a pair (under the added assumption that $f(x, y)$ is $1 - 1$).

THEOREM 23. If $(\tilde{\gamma}_1, \tilde{\gamma}_2)$ is doubly productive then $(\tilde{\gamma}_1, \tilde{\gamma}_2)$ is completely doubly productive (relative to the collection of all disjoint pairs of r.e. sets).

PROOF. Suppose $(\tilde{\gamma}_1, \tilde{\gamma}_2)$ is doubly productive. Then (γ_1, γ_2) is uniformly doubly universal. We again apply Lemma B, letting Σ be the collection of all disjoint pairs of r.e. sets, and noting that if $(A, B) \in \Sigma$ then $(A^*, B^*) \in \Sigma$.

§20. A GENERALIZATION OF EFFECTIVE INSEPARABILITY

Muchnik [12] generalizes the notion of recursive inseparability to pairs of sets which are not necessarily disjoint. He calls a pair (γ_1, γ_2) recursively inseparable iff it has the property that there exists no r.e. supersets (ω_i, ω_j) of (γ_1, γ_2) whose intersection is $\gamma_1 \cap \gamma_2$ and whose union is the whole set of numbers. Equivalently, (γ_1, γ_2) is recursively inseparable iff for every pair (ω_i, ω_j) of supersets whose intersection is $\gamma_1 \cap \gamma_2$, there is a number outside $\omega_i \cup \omega_j$. It is obvious that when γ_1, γ_2 are disjoint, this definition agrees with the former definition of R.I.

We shall analogously generalize the notion of "effective" inseparability for pairs not necessarily disjoint. We shall say that (γ_1, γ_2) is effectively inseparable iff there is a recursive function $\delta(x, y)$ [which we will again call an E.I. function for the pair] such that for every pair (ω_i, ω_j) of supersets whose intersection is $(\gamma_1 \cap \gamma_2)$, $\delta(i, j)$ is a number outside $\omega_i \cup \omega_j$.

It is a trivial matter to modify the proof of Proposition 4 (§4) to obtain:

PROPOSITION 4'. Let (A_1, A_2) be reducible to (B_1, B_2).

Then if (A_1, A_2) is E.I. (without necessarily being disjoint), so is (B_1, B_2).

We next show

THEOREM 12'. For any two sets (α, β) (whether disjoint or not)
(a) If $(\tilde{\alpha}, \tilde{\beta})$ is doubly productive, then (α, β) is E.I.
(b) If (α, β) is E.I. and α, β are both r.e., then $(\tilde{\alpha}, \tilde{\beta})$ is doubly productive.

PROOF. The proof of (b) is a trivial modification of the proof of Theorem 12 - (b). The proof of (a) is, however, more delicate, and runs as follows

Suppose $(\tilde{\alpha}, \tilde{\beta})$ is doubly productive under $g(x, y)$. We wish to show that (β, α) is E.I. (which, of course implies that (α, β) is E.I.). Let ω_i, ω_j be r.e. supersets of β, α respectively whose intersection is $\alpha \cap \beta$. We wish to effectively find a number outside $\omega_i \cup \omega_j$. Now, we cannot (as with Theorem 12) simply apply $g(x, y)$ to (i, j), since ω_i, ω_j intersect (if α, β do). But we can <u>first</u> find disjoint r.e. supersets of $(\omega_i - \omega_j), (\omega_j - \omega_i)$ [cf. §13, Chapter IV, page 90]. Moreover the process of finding these sets is easily seen to be effective — i.e., there exist recursive functions $t_1(x_1, x_2), t_2(x_1, x_2)$ such that for every i, j the sets $\omega_{t_1(i, j)}, \omega_{t_2(i, j)}$ are disjoint and respective supersets of $(\omega_i - \omega_j), (\omega_j - \omega_i)$. [To see this, just use the iteration theorem on the r.e. relation $(Ey)[M_1(x_1, x, y) \wedge (Ay')_{\leq y} \sim M_2(x_2, x, y)]$, and on the r.e. relation $(Ey)[M_2(x_2, x, y) \wedge (Ay')_{\leq y} \sim M_1(x_1, x_2, y)]$.]

The sets $\omega_{t_1(i, j)}, \omega_{t_2(i, j)}$ are respectively disjoint from $(\alpha - \beta), (\beta - \alpha)$, so $g[t_1(i, j), t_2(i, j)]$ is outside all 4 sets $\omega_{t_1(i, j)}, \omega_{t_2(i, j)}, \alpha, \beta$. Hence this number is outside ω_i and ω_j. Thus $g[t_1(x, y), t_2(x, y)]$ is an E.I function for the pair (β, α). This completes the proof.

From Proposition 4' it follows that a doubly universal pair (γ_1, γ_2) is E.I. (whether disjoint or not), since we can take some E.I. pair of r.e. sets and reduce it to (γ_1, γ_2). And from Theorem 12' and Theorem 16 follows:

THEOREM 19'. Every E.I. pair of r.e. sets (whether disjoint or not) is doubly universal. Hence a pair of r.e. sets is E.I. iff it is D.U.

It if obvious that if (α, β) is E.I. then so is every pair of supersets whose intersection is the same as that of α and β. Hence Theorem 19' yields:

THEOREM 20'. If (α, β) is doubly universal, then so is every pair of r.e. supersets whose intersection is the same as that of α and β.

#E. DOUBLE ISOMORPHISM

§21. DOUBLE ISOMORPHISM

We shall say that the pair (A_1, A_2) is 1 - 1 equivalent to (B_1, B_2) iff each pair is 1 - 1 reducible to the other. And we shall say that (A_1, A_2) is (doubly) isomorphic to (B_1, B_2) iff there is a recursive permutation $f(x)$ which simultaneously maps A_1 onto B_1 and A_2 onto B_2. We write "$(A_1, A_2) \equiv (B_1, B_2)$", "$(A_1, A_2) \cong (B_1, B_2)$" to denote these respective conditions.

If $(A_1, A_2) \cong (B_1, B_2)$ then of course $A_1 \cong B_1$ and $A_2 \cong B_2$. The converse however is not necessarily true. To show this take (A_1, A_2) to be disjoint creative sets which are E.I.; take (B_1, B_2) to be disjoint creative sets which are not E.I. (cf. discussion at the end of §12). Then clearly (A_1, A_2) is not isomorphic to $(B_1, B_2$. Yet $A_1 \cong B_1$ and $A_2 \cong B_2$ (by Myhill's theorem that any two creative sets are isomorphic).

Myhill [14] proved that if two sets are 1 - 1 equivalent then they are isomorphic. The purpose of #E is to generalize this result to ordered pairs -- i.e., to prove that if $(A_1, A_2) \equiv (B_1, B_2)$ then $(A_1, A_2) \cong (B_1, B_2)$. From this and Theorem 17 we immediately get the result that up to double isomorphism there is only one disjoint E.I. pair of r.e. sets (and also that there is only one E.I.$^+$ pair of r.e. sets).

FINITE CORRESPONDENCES. Let M be a finite sequence of pairs $\{(x_i, y_i)\}$ which is 1 - 1 in the sense that for each i, j, $x_i = x_j \longleftrightarrow y_i = y_j$. Myhill [14] calls M a finite correspondence between two sets A and B iff for each i, $x_i \in A \longleftrightarrow y_i \in B$. Myhill then proves [Theorem 17] that if AR_1B then there exists an effective method whereby given any finite correspondence $((x_1, y_1), \ldots, (x_k, y_k))$ between A and B, and any number m, one can effectively find a number n such that $((x_1, y_1), \ldots, (x_k, y_k), (m, n))$ is likewise a finite correspondence between A and B. Now, if we look carefully through Myhill's proof, we note that the process for finding the desired number n is independent of the sets A and B; rather it depends only on the function f which is a 1 - 1 reduction of A to B (as well, of course, as an M and m). We thus obtain the following more pregnant statement:

PROPOSITION 9. Let f be a 1 - 1 recursive function. Then there exists an effective method whereby given any finite 1 - 1 sequence

M; viz. $\{(x_1, y_1), \ldots, (x_k, y_k)\}$, and any number m, one can effectively find a number n such that the following holds: For any two sets A and B, if f is a $1-1$ reduction of A to B and if $\{(x_i, y_i)\}$ is a correspondence between A and B, then $\{(x_1, y_1), \ldots, (x_k, y_k), (m, n)\}$ is likewise a correspondence between A and B.

PROOF. If for some $i \leq k$, $m = x_i$, then take $n = y_i$. This case is trivial. Suppose now that m does not occur amongst the x_i. Let t be the number of distinct numbers amongst the x_i; then there are $t + 1$ distinct numbers amongst $x_1, \ldots, x_k, m$. Also, since M is $1-1$, there are exactly t distinct numbers amongst the y_i. Consider now the set $f(m), f(x_1), \ldots, f(x_k)$. There are exactly $t + 1$ distinct numbers in this set (since f is $1-1$). Hence at least one of them lies outside the set of $\{y_i\}$. If $f(m)$ lies outside this set take $n = f(m)$. This case is again trivial. If $f(m)$ lies amongst the y_i, then there is a sequence of numbers $i_1, i_2, \ldots, i_r [2 \leq r \leq k]$ such that}

$$
\begin{aligned}
f(m) &= y_{i_1} \\
f(x_{i_1}) &= y_{i_2} \\
&\vdots \\
f(x_{i_{r-1}}) &= y_{i_r} \\
f(x_{i_r}) &= n \quad (n \text{ is outside the } y_i)
\end{aligned}
$$

The process of finding n is evidently effective. Now let A and B be any two sets such that f is a reduction of A to B and M is a correspondence between A and B. Let M' be the sequence $\{(x_1, y_1), \ldots, (x_k, y_k), (m, n)\}$. It is clear that M' is $1-1$. We must show that M' is likewise a correspondence between A and B. To this end we must show that $m \in A \longleftrightarrow n \in B$.

If $m \in \{x_i\}$, the case is trivial. Likewise if $f(m) \notin \{y_i\}$, the case is trivial. In the final case, we have:

$$
\begin{aligned}
m \in A &\longleftrightarrow y_{i_1} \in B && \text{[Since f is a reduction of A to B]} \\
&\longleftrightarrow x_{i_1} \in A && \text{[Since M is a correspondence between A and B].} \\
&\longleftrightarrow y_{i_2} \in B \\
&\quad \vdots \\
&\longleftrightarrow x_{i_{r-1}} \in A \\
&\longleftrightarrow y_{i_{r-1}} \in B \\
&\longleftrightarrow x_{i_2} \in A \\
&\longleftrightarrow n \in B
\end{aligned}
$$

Q.E.D.

We shall define $\pi(f, M, m)$ to be the number n obtained from f and M as in the preceding proof. Also for any finite sequence M; viz. $(x_1, y_1), \ldots, (x_n, y_n)$ we let M^{-1} be the sequence $(y_1, x_1), \ldots, (y_n, x_n)$. Clearly if M is a correspondence from A to B, then M^{-1} is a correspondence from B to A.

§22. 1 - 1 EQUIVALENCE AND DOUBLE ISOMORPHISM

Myhill [14] then shows [Theorem 18] how given any two sets A and B and any two recursive functions f and g such that f is a 1 - 1 reduction of A to B and g is a 1 - 1 reduction of B to A, a recursive permutation h can be constructed which is an isomorphism between A and B. Again, Myhill's construction of h does not depend on the sets A and B, but only on the functions f and g. Thus we can assert:

PROPOSITION 10. Let f and g each be 1 - 1 recursive functions. Then there is a recursive permutation h such that for any two sets A and B, if f is a reduction of A to B and g is a reduction of B to A then h is an isomorphism between A and B.

PROOF. Let us say that a finite 1 - 1 correspondence M dovetails with (f, g) iff the following condition holds: For any two sets A and B such that f is a reduction of A to B and g is a reduction of B to A, M is a correspondence between A and B.

We construct an infinite sequence $\{(1, y_1), (x_1, 1), (2, y_2), (x_2, 2) \ldots (n, y_n), (x_n, n) \ldots\}$ as follows:

We set $y_1 = f(1)$. It is obvious that $\{(1, y_1)\}$ dovetails with (f, g). Suppose M: viz. $\{(1, y_1), \ldots, (n, y_n)\}$ $(n > 1)$ has been constructed which dovetails with (f, g). Set $x_n = \pi(g, M^{-1}, n)$. Then it is obvious, by Proposition 9, that the correspondence $\{(1, y_1), \ldots, (n, y_n), (x_n, n)\}$ dovetails with (f, g). Suppose M; viz. $\{(1, y_1), \ldots, (x_n, n)\}$ has been constructed which dovetails with (f, g). Set $y_{n+1} = \pi(f, M, n + 1)$. Then the correspondence $\{(1, y_1, \ldots, (x_n, n), (n + 1, y_{n+1})\}$ dovetails with (f, g).

Let $h(x)$ be that number y such that (x, y) occurs in the above sequence. It is easily checked that h is recursive, and of course h is a permutation. And for any two sets A, B such that f is a reduction of A to B and g is a reduction of B to A, h is an isomorphism between A and B.

THEOREM 24. If $(A_1, A_2) \equiv (B_1, B_2)$ then $(A_1, A_2) \cong (B_1, B_2)$.

PROOF. Immediate from Proposition 10.

THEOREM 25. Up to double isomorphism there is only one disjoint pair of doubly universal sets which are r.e. That is to say, if (γ_1, γ_2) and (γ_1', γ_2') are two such pairs, then (γ_1, γ_2) is doubly isomorphic to (γ_1', γ_2').

PROOF. In both cases (a) and (b), the hypothesis implies that each of the pairs (γ_1, γ_2), (γ_1', γ_2') is $1 - 1$ reducible to the other. Results then follow by Theorem 24.

THEOREM 26.[1] Up to double isomorphism there is only one disjoint pair of r.e. sets which is E.I.

PROOF. By Theorems 2 , and 19.

§23. DOUBLE ISOMORPHISM OF ROSSER SYSTEMS

We shall call two systems Q, Q' <u>isomorphic</u> iff T_0 is isomorphic to T_0'. We shall say that Z is <u>doubly isomorphic</u> to Z' iff (T_0, R_0) is isomorphic to (T_0', R_0'). We might call Q a <u>Gödel system</u> iff every r.e. set is representable in it. Any formal Gödel system is creative, hence any two such systems are isomorphic -- this is Myhill's result. We now have the "double analogue" of this result which is

THEOREM 27. Any two consistent formal Rosser systems are doubly isomorphic.

PROOF. If Z and Z' are both consistent formal Rosser systems then (T_0, R_0) and (T_0', R_0') are both disjoint E.I. pairs of r.e. sets (by Theorem 4). Result then follows by Theorem 26.

---

[1] This was first proved by Muchnik [13] and independently by the present author [30], [31].

SUPPLEMENT

APPLICATIONS TO MATHEMATICAL LOGIC

In this supplement we first give a very brief introductory sketch of the structure of those systems (call "theories" by Tarski) whose logical basis includes at least the first order predicate calculus. We then discuss the applications of Chapters III, IV, V to these systems. Some of these applications are well known; others are new.

We have organized this material so that the various sections can be read immediately following those chapters which they presuppose; we indicate in advance just what is needed for each section. The reader familiar with the definition of "theory" can skip §1.

Sections §1 - §4 [Presupposes #A of Chapter III].

§1. THEORIES

By a theory (T) we shall mean a collection of the following items which obey the conditions stated alongside.

(1) A finite alphabet K together with an admissible[1] Gödel numbering g of $\underline{K}$ onto N.

(2) A recursive[2] subset of $\underline{K}$ whose elements are called (well formed) formulas. Formulas will be denoted by "F", "G", with or without subscripts.

---

[1] The admissability of g is required in §6 on, as otherwise our results on undecidability, though still correct as stated, would no longer mean what they usually do -- i.e., the term "undecidability" would have a non-standard meaning.

[2] As in #B of Chapter III, we refer to an attribute of expressions of K as being "recursive" meaning that the corresponding attribute of Gödel numbers is recursive. Under the assumed admissability of g, "recursive" when applied to word attributes can alternatively be read "solvable over K". We might remark that none of the conditions of recursiveness which appear in our definition of a theory will be used before we come to §6.

(3) A 1 - 1 function which assigns to each formula F a formula $\sim F$ (also written F') called the negation of F. The set of all ordered pairs $(F, \sim F)$ is to be recursive.

(4) A 1 - 1 function which assigns to each ordered pair (F, G) of formulas a formula $F \wedge G$, called the conjunction of F and G. The set of all triples $(F, G, F \wedge G)$ is to be recursive. We write $F \vee G$ for $\sim(\sim F \wedge \sim G)$; $F \supset G$ for $\sim(F \wedge \sim G)$ and $F \equiv G$ for $(F \supset G) \wedge (G \supset F)$.

(5) A denumerable sequence $(x_1, x_2, \ldots, x_i, \ldots)$ of words (in K), called (free individual) variables. No variable is to be a formula. No two distinct variables which occur in the same word may overlap. The function $f(n) = g(x_n)$ is to be recursive. The set of all variables is to be recursive. For any variable x and formulas F and G, the following conditions must hold:

(i) x is part of $\sim F$ iff x is part of F

(ii) x is part of $F \wedge G$ iff x is part of F or x is part of G. For any word X, variable x and word Y, by X^x_Y is meant the result of replacing all occurrences of x in X by Y. The following conditions must hold:

(iii) $(\sim F)^x_Y = \sim (F^x_Y)$

(iv) $(F \wedge G)^x_Y = F^x_Y \wedge G^x_Y$.

(6) A 1 - 1 function which assigns to each formula F and each variable x a formula (Ex)F, called the existential quantification of F with respect to x. The set of all triples (F, x, (Ex)F) is to be recursive. The variable x is not part of the formula (Ex)F.[1] For any variable $y \neq x$, y is part of (Ex)F iff y is part of F. The following conditions must hold:

(i) $((Ex)F)^x_Y = (Ex)F$;

(ii) If $y \neq x$ then $((Ex)F)^y_Y = (Ex)(F^y_Y)$. We write (Ax)F to mean $\sim((Ex)(\sim F))$. The formula (Ax)F is called the universal quantification of F with respect to x. By a closed formula or a sentence we shall mean a formula in which no (free) variable occurs as a part.

(7) A 1 - 1 function which assigns to each number (positive integer) n a word $\bar{n}$ called the numeral associated with n. The function $f(n) = g(\bar{n})$ is to be recursive. No numeral is a variable or a formula. If x is part of F then $F^x_{\bar{n}}$ is a formula.

(8) A set A of sentences called axioms of (T).

Let W be any set of sentences of (T). We shall call W a perfect set iff it has the following three properties:

---

[1] We are thinking of those formulations of first order logic in which the bound variables are distinct from the free variables.

(1) For any sentence X, the sentence $\sim X$ is in W iff X is not in W (consistency + completeness).

(2) A sentence $X \wedge Y$ is in W iff X and Y are both in W.

(3) A sentence $(Ex)F$ is in W iff there is at least one number n such that $F^x_{\bar{n}}$ is in W.

A sentence X is said to be a logical consequence of a set W of sentences iff X is in every perfect superset of W. We say that X is logically valid[1] iff X is an element of every perfect set -- equivalently, iff X is a logical consequence of the empty set of sentences. We now define the set T of theorems of (T) to be the set of all sentences which are logical consequences of the axiom set A.

REMARKS. The definition of logical validity is, of course, non-constructive, due to the non-finitary nature of condition (3) of the definition of a perfect set. Nevertheless the set L of logically valid sentences turns out to be recursively enumerable (by Gödel's completeness theorem or, alternatively, Herbrand's Theorem). Many formal axiom systems for the set L can be found in various introductions to mathematical logic (e.g., Church [2]). We do not wish to take the space here to give any such axiomatic treatment; our arguments will rather have an informal character.

REPRESENTATION SYSTEMS ASSOCIATED WITH THEORIES. By $X(Y_1, \ldots, Y_n)$ we shall mean the result of simultaneously substituting Y_1 for $x_1, \ldots, Y_n$ for x_n in X. A formula F of (T) will be called a predicate of degree n iff the (free) variables $x_1, \ldots, x_n$ are each a part of F and no other variable is part of F. If F is a predicate of degree n then it is obvious that for any numbers $a_1, \ldots, a_n$, the formula $F(\bar{a}_1, \ldots, \bar{a}_n)$ (which we will also write $F(a_1, \ldots, a_n)$) must be a sentence.

With each theory (T) we now associate a relational representation system $Z(T)$ in the obvious manner; viz., $Z(T)$ is the system $(E, S, T, R, \mathscr{P}, \Phi)$, where $E = \underline{K}$, S is the set of sentences of (T), T is the set of theorems of (T), R is the set of sentences whose negation is a theorem of (T), $\mathscr{P}$ is the set of predicates of (T) together with the function which assigns them their degrees, and Φ is the function: $\Phi(X, a_1, \ldots, a_n) = X(\bar{a}_1, \ldots, \bar{a}_n)$. By representability, complete representability, definability, separability in (T) we mean the same notions respectively applied to the associated representation system $Z(T)$. Likewise with the notions of completeness,

[1] We are here using "logically valid" to mean logically valid in the denumerable domain of the positive integers.

consistency and normality. We call (T) a Rosser theory iff Z(T) is a Rosser system. We refer to the sets T_0, R_0 as the nuclei of (T), as with the case Z(T). All theorems which we have proved for representation systems in general obviously hold for those particular representation systems which arise from theories. We note that every theory (T) is symmetric in the sense of §7, #A (i.e., Z(T) is symmetric). [This is due to the fact that for any sentence X, the sentences X and $\sim(\sim X)$ are logically equivalent (i.e., each is a logical consequence of the other). Thus X is provable iff $\sim X$ is refutable (and of course, X is refutable iff $\sim X$ is provable by definition of "refutable").]

§2. CALCULABILITY OF FUNCTIONS; NORMALITY

We shall say that a function f(x) is calculable or definable in (T) iff there is a predicate $F(x_1, x_2)$ such that the following conditions hold:

(i) $F(x_1, x_2)$ defines in (T) the relation $f(x) = y$;

(ii) For any numbers m, n such that $n = f(m)$, and for every unary predicate $G(x_1)$, the sentence $(Ex_2)[F(\bar{m}, x_2) \wedge G(x_2)] \supset G(\bar{n})$ is provable in (T).

Such a formula $F(x_1, x_2)$ will be said to calculate or define the function f(x) in (T).[1] It is trivial to verify that the inverse image of any set representable in (T) under a function definable in (T) is representable in (T); more specifically if $G(x_1)$ represents A in (T) and if $F(x_1, x_2)$ defines the function f(x) in (T), then $f^{-1}(A)$ is represented in (T) by the predicate $(Ex_2)[F(x_1, x_2) \wedge G(x_2)]$. From this it follows that if the diagonal function D(x) is definable in (T) then (T) must be normal (i.e., if W_0 is definable in (T) so is W^*). It is also trivial to verify that if $G(x_1)$ completely represents A in (T) and if $F(x_1, x_2)$ defines f(x) in (T), then the formula $(Ex_2)[F(x_1, x_2) \wedge G(x_2)]$ completely represents the set $f^{-1}(A)$. Hence if T is consistent, then the inverse image of any representable set under a definable function is in turn definable in (T). In particular if the diagonal function D(x) is definable in (T) then for any set W of expressions, if W_0 is definable in (T) so is W^* (under the assumption that (T) is consistent). Then by Theorem 3 (Ch. III) it follows that if D(x) is definable in (T) then

[1] In Tarski [32, p. 45] a definition of definability of functions is given for theories containing an identity predicate. The above definition, due to Hilary Putnam and the author, generalizes this notion for theories with or without identity. [For theories with identity, the two definitions are, of course, equivalent.]

R_0 is not definable in (T) (this latter result is due to Tarski). In fact by using the second part of statement (ii) of Theorem 7 (Ch. III) (which was established by using the Rosser-like argument involving the second diagonalization lemma, we get the stronger result that if $D(x)$ is definable in (T) then no superset of T_0 or R_0 disjoint from the other is definable in (T).

§3. ω-CONSISTENCY; ENUMERABILITY WITHIN (T); GÖDEL'S THEOREM

If (T) contains a predicate $F(x_1)$ such that $(Ex_1)F(x_1)$ is provable but such that for every number m, the sentence F(m) is refutable, then (T) is called ω-<u>inconsistent</u>; otherwise (T) is called ω-<u>consistent</u>. If (T) is ω-inconsistent it is not necessarily (simply) inconsistent; (examples of consistent theories which are ω-inconsistent are well known). However, if a theory is simply inconsistent then it is certainly ω-inconsistent, since every sentence is then provable.

Let M(x, y) be a binary relation and A a number set. We shall say that M <u>enumerates</u> A iff A is the existential quantification (domain) of M. We shall say that A is <u>enumerable in the theory</u> (T) iff there is a formula (predicate) $F(x_1, x_2)$ which defines a relation M(x, y) which enumerates A; such a formula $F(x_1, x_2)$ will be said to enumerate A in (T).

LEMMA A. If A is enumerable in (T) and (T) is ω-consistent then A is representable in (T).

PROOF. Let $F(x_1, x_2)$ define a relation M(x, y) whose domain is A. Let $H(x_1)$ be the formula $(Ex_2)F(x_1, x_2)$. We wish to show that if (T) is ω-consistent then $H(x_1)$ represents A in (T).

(a) Suppose that (T) is simply consistent. Then $F(x_1, x_2)$ completely represents M(x, y). Suppose $n \in A$. Then for some number m the relation M(n, m) holds. Hence $F(\bar{n}, \bar{m})$ is provable in (T). But the formula $H(\bar{n})$; viz. $(Ex_2)F(\bar{n}, x_2)$ is a logical consequence of $F(\bar{n}, \bar{m})$ and hence is provable. Thus if (T) is simply consistent then $H(x_1)$ represents some superset of A.

(b) Suppose that (T) is also ω-consistent. We must then show that if $H(\bar{n})$ is provable then n is really in A. Well, let $(Ex_2)F(\bar{n}, x_2)$ be provable. Then by ω-consistency there is at least one number m such that $F(\bar{n}, \bar{m})$ is not refutable. But since $F(x_1, x_2)$ is a numeralwise decidable predicate, $F(\bar{n}, \bar{m})$ must then be provable. Hence M(n, m) holds (since $F(x_1, x_2)$ defines this relation). Hence $n \in A$. This completes the proof.

Theorem 7 (iii) (Chapter III) and Lemma A at once yields

THEOREM A. (After Gödel). If either R^* or T^* is enumerable in (T) and if (T) is ω-consistent then (T) is incomplete.

The above theorem is perhaps more familiar in the following form: Let Pf be a collection of sequences of sentences of (T), each sequence being called a proof of its last term; let Pf be such that a sentence is a theorem of (T) iff it is the last term of some proof. In addition to the Gödel numbering of the expressions of (T), let there be a 1 - 1 mapping which assigns to each proof a number called the Gödel number of the proof. Let A(x, y) be the set of all ordered pairs (x, y) such that y is the Gödel number of a proof of $E_x(x)$; let B(x, y) be the set of all ordered pairs (x, y) such that y is the Gödel number of a proof of the negation of $E_x(x)$.

THEOREM A_1. If either A(x, y) or B(x, y) is definable in (T) and if (T) is ω-consistent, then (T) is incomplete.

PROOF. The relation A(x, y) enumerates the set T^*; the relation B(x, y) enumerates the set R^*. Thus the statement that A(x, y) is definable in (T) is but a special way of saying that the set T^* is enumerable in (T); similarly if B(x, y) is definable in (T) then R^* is enumerable in (T). Result then follows by Theorem A.

DISCUSSION. We can now see just where ω-consistency enters in Gödel's argument. For the class of theories considered by Gödel, the sets T^* and R^* were shown to be enumerable in the theory without the assumption of ω-consistency (since the relations A(x, y), B(x, y) were shown to be definable in the theory, without this assumption). But ω-consistency was necessary to pass from enumerability of these sets within the theory to representability within the theory.

§4. ROSSER'S CONSTRUCTION

We now consider a theory (T) containing a binary predicate -- which we will write "$x_1 \leq x_2$" -- such that for all formulas F(x), $F_1(x)$, $F_2(x)$ and every number n the following two conditions hold:

C_1: $F(\bar{1}), F(\bar{2}), \ldots, F(\bar{n})$ are all provable iff the formula $(Ax)\,[x \leq \bar{n} \supset F(x)]$ is provable.

C_2: If the sentences $(Ax)\,[x \leq \bar{n} \supset F_1(x)]$ and $(Ax)\,[\bar{n} \leq x \supset F_2(x)]$ are both provable then so is the sentence $(Ax)\,[F_1(x) \vee F_2(x)]$.

REMARK. For theories (T) containing an identity predicate $x_1 = x_2$ satisfying the usual axioms (a consequence of which is that all sentences of the form $F(\bar{n}) \longleftrightarrow (Ax)\,[x = \bar{n} \supset F(x)]$ are provable), it is readily seen that C_1 and C_2 are respective consequences of the properties:

C_1': For every n the sentence $(Ax)(x = \bar{1} \vee x = \bar{2} \vee \ldots \vee x = \bar{n}) \longleftrightarrow x \leq \bar{n})$ is provable.

C_2': For every n the sentence $(Ax)\ [x \leq \bar{n} \vee \bar{n} \leq x]$ is provable.

LEMMA B [After Rosser]. Let (T) be a theory obeying conditions C_1 and C_2. Then for any two sets A, B which are <u>enumerable</u> in (T), the set (A - B) is strongly separable from (B - A) in (T). Thus for such a theory (T), if A and B are disjoint sets which are enumerable in (T), then (A, B) is strongly separable in (T).

PROOF. Let $F_1(x_1, x_2)$ define in (T) a relation $R_1(x, y)$ which enumerates A; let $F_2(x_1, x_2)$ define $R_2(x, y)$ which enumerates B; let $G(x_1)$ be the predicate $(Ex_2)\ [F_1(x_1, x_2) \wedge (Ay)\ [y \leq x_2 \supset \sim F_2(x_1, y)]]$. We show that $G(x_1)$ strongly separates the pair (A - B), (B - A) in (T).

(a) Suppose $n \in (A - B)$. Since $n \in A$ then for some m the relation $R_1(n, m)$ holds and hence $F_1(\bar{n}, \bar{m})$ is provable. Since $n \notin B$ then for every number i the relation $(\tilde{R}_2(n, i)$ holds, hence $\sim F_2(\bar{n}, \bar{1})$ is provable. Thus $\sim F_2(\bar{n}, \bar{1}), \ldots, \sim F_2(\bar{n}, \bar{m})$ are all provable, so the sentence $(Ay)\ [y \leq \bar{m} \supset \sim F_2(\bar{n}, y)]$ is provable by condition C_1. So the sentences $F_1(\bar{n}, \bar{m})$ and $(Ay)\ [y \leq \bar{m} \supset \sim F_2(n, y)]$ are both provable. Hence the conjunction $F_1(\bar{n}, \bar{m}) \wedge (Ay)\ [y \leq m \supset \sim F_2(\bar{n}, y)]$ is provable. Therefore the sentence $(Ex_2)\ [F_1(\bar{n}, x_2) \wedge (Ay)\ [y \leq \bar{m} \supset \sim F_2(\bar{n}, y)]]$ is provable — i.e., $G(\bar{n})$ is provable.

(b) Suppose $n \in (B - A)$. Since $n \in B$ then for some m the sentence $F_2(\bar{n}, \bar{m})$ is provable. Therefore the following sentence, being a logical consequence of $F_2(\bar{n}, \bar{m})$, is provable:

(i) $(Ax_2)\ [\bar{m} \leq x_2 \supset (Ey)\ [y \leq x_2 \wedge F_2(\bar{n}, y)]]$.

Since $n \notin A$, then by the same method as the proof of (a), the following sentence is provable:

(ii) $(Ax_2)\ [x_2 \leq \bar{m} \supset \sim F_1(\bar{n}, x_2)]$.

By (i), (ii) and property C_2, the sentence $(Ax_2)\ [\sim F_1(\bar{n}, x_2) \vee (Ey)\ [y \leq x_2 \wedge F_2(\bar{n}, y)]]$ is provable. But the latter sentence is logically equivalent to the sentence $\sim G(\bar{n})$. Hence $G(\bar{n})$ is refutable.

Theorem 7, (iii) (Chapter III) and Lemma B at once yield

THEOREM B (After Rosser). If T^* and R^* are both enumerable in (T) and if (T) satisfies conditions C_1 and C_2 then (T) is either <u>simply</u> inconsistent or incomplete.

Again we can refer to the relations A(x, y) and B(x, y) of Theorem A_1, and state Theorem B in the more familiar form:

THEOREM B_1. If (T) is a simply consistent theory in which the relations A(x, y) and B(x, y) are definable and if (T) satisfies conditions C_1 and C_2 then (T) is incomplete.

REMARK. Just as ω-consistency enables us to pass from the enumerability of a set within a theory to the representability of the set within the theory, so do conditions C_1, C_2 jointly enable us to pass from the enumerability of disjoint sets α, β within (T) to the strong separation of the pair (α, β) within (T).

Section §5 - [Presupposes the remainder of Chapter III].

§5. GÖDEL THEORIES AND ROSSER THEORIES

We are calling (T) a Gödel theory iff all r.e. sets are representable in (T). We know that every Gödel theory is undecidable and that every formal Gödel theory is incomplete.

We recall that if an attribute is definable in (T) then it is definable in every extension of (T)[1] (this is of course not true for "representable" rather than "definable"). Hence every set enumerable within a theory (T) is enumerable within every extension of (T). Hence, by Lemma A, if a set α is enumerable within (T) then α is representable within every ω-consistent extension of (T). We then have

THEOREM C. If all r.e. sets are enumerable within (T) then every ω-consistent extension of (T) is a Gödel theory.

ROSSER THEORIES. Lemma B at once gives

THEOREM D. Every theory (T) in which all r.e. sets are enumerable and which satisfies conditions C_1 and C_2 is a Rosser theory.

REMARK. Lemma B in fact gives the apparently stronger conclusion that if (T) is any theory which obeys the hypothesis of Theorem D, then (T) has the property that for any two r.e. sets α, β the pair ((α - β), (β - α)) is strongly separable in (T). However any Rosser theory has this property. For suppose that (T) is a Rosser theory and that α, β are any r.e. sets. By §13, Chapter IV, there exist disjoint r.e. supersets of (α - β), (β - α); these supersets can be strongly separated in the Rosser theory (T), so the smaller sets (α - β), (β - α) are then strongly separated in (T).

---

[1] By an extension of (T) we shall understand a theory (T') whose sentences are the same as those of (T) and whose theorems include those of (T). [The refutable sentences of (T') will then include the refutable sentences of (T).]

5.1. ROSSER THEORIES FOR RELATIONS. What we have so far termed a "Rosser theory" let us now more specifically term a Rosser theory for sets. Let us call (T) a Rosser theory for n-ary relations iff every disjoint pair (R_1, R_2) of r.e. relations of degree n is strongly separable in (T) (in the sense that there is a predicate $F(x_1, \ldots, x_n)$ of (T) which is provable for all n-tuples in R_1 and refutable for all n-tuples in R_2). Let us also say that a relation $R(x_1, \ldots, x_n)$ is enumerable in (T) iff R is expressible in the form $(Ey)\, S(x_1, \ldots, x_n, y)$ where S is a relation which is definable in (T). It is trivial to verify that Lemmas A and B hold good for A and B relations (of the same degree), rather than sets. Hence Theorem D can be stated in the more general form:

THEOREM D'. Every theory (T) in which all r.e. attributes of degree n are enumerable and which satisfies conditions C_1 and C_2 is a Rosser theory for n-ary attributes.

We note that if (T) is a Rosser theory for n-ary relations then certainly all recursive relations of degree n are definable in (T). Hence if (T) is a Rosser theory for relations of degree n + 1 then all recursive functions $f(x_1, \ldots, x_n)$ are definable in (T).[1] So if we wish to show that all recursive functions are definable in a given theory (T), we obtain a still better result if we can show that for every n, (T) is a Rosser theory for n-ary relations.

We might also remark that if (T) is a Rosser theory for relations of degree n then for any two r.e. relations R_1, R_2 of degree n the pair $((R_1 - R_2), (R_2 - R_1))$ is strongly separable in (T). For it can be proved (analogously to §13, Chapter IV) that there exists disjoint r.e. relations S_1, S_2 such that $(R_1 - R_2) \subseteq S_1$ and $(R_2 - R_1) \subseteq S_2$.

5.2. SUB-BASES FOR R.E. ATTRIBUTES. It is easy to verify that for any consistent theory (T), the collection of all attributes definable in (T) is closed under union, intersection, complementation and all explicit transformations. Moreover if (T) also obeys condition C_1, then the collection of attributes definable in (T) is also closed under finite quantification. The definable attributes of such a theory (T) are thus closed under constructive definability. This means that if $\mathscr{S}$ is any sub-basis for the collection of recursively enumerable attributes and if (T) is a consistent theory obeying C_1 and in which each element of $\mathscr{S}$ is definable, then every r.e. attribute is enumerable in (T). We thus have:

---

1 Definable in the sense that the relation $f(x_1, \ldots, x_n) = y$ is definable in (T); this does not however necessarily mean that $f(x_1, \ldots, x_n)$ is calculable in (T) in the sense of §2.

THEOREM E. Let (T) be a consistent theory in which the elements of some sub-basis $\mathcal{S}$ are all definable. Then

(a) If (T) obeys condition C_1 then every ω-consistent extension of (T) is a Gödel theory (in fact all r.e. attributes of all degrees are then representable in every ω-consistent extension of (T)).

(b) If (T) obeys conditions C_1 and C_2 then every simply consistent extension of (T) is a Rosser theory (both for sets and for relations of all degrees).

Sections §6 - §8 [Presupposes #B of Chapter IV.]

§6. THEORIES IN WHICH PLUS AND TIMES ARE DEFINABLE

It was shown in Chapter IV that plus and times form a sub-basis for the r.e. attributes. We thus have

THEOREM E'. Let (T) be a theory in which plus and times are definable. Then (a) and (b) of Theorem E hold.

REMARK. Likewise (a) and (b) hold for any theory in which dyadic concatenation is definable.

The fact that plus and times form a sub-basis for the r.e. attributes of course implies the weaker fact that every r.e. attribute is arithmetic. This latter has the following interesting consequence:

THEOREM F. Let (T) be a <u>saturated</u> theory whose representable attributes coincide with the arithmetic attributes. Then

(a) (T) is a normal theory.

(b) The set T_0 is not arithmetic. [Tarski's theorem].

(c) (T) is not a formal theory.

(d) Every formal sub-theory of (T) contains an undecidable sentence.

PROOF.

(a) It is trivial to verify that the inverse image of an arithmetic set under an arithmetic function (i.e., a function $f(x)$ such that the relation $f(x) = y$ is arithmetic) is again an arithmetic set. Since the diagonal function $D(x)$ is recursive, it is also arithmetic. Hence if W_0 is arithmetic so is W^* (which equals $D^{-1}(W_0)$) -- i.e., (T) is normal.

(b) Since (T) is assumed saturated then (T) is complemented -- i.e., the complement of every set (in fact every attribute) representable in (T) is again representable in (T). Then since (T) is normal, T_0 is not representable in (T) by Theorem 1.1 - Chapter III. This means that T_0 is not arithmetic.

(c) Since T_0 is not arithmetic it certainly is not r.e. So (T) is not a formal theory.

(d) Let (T_1) be a formal sub-theory of (T). Then, T_1 is r.e. but T is not r.e. Hence $T_1 \subseteq T$ but $T_1 \neq T$. So there is a sentence $X \in (T - T_1)$. Clearly $X \notin T_1$. Since $X \in T$ then $X \notin R$ (by consistency of (T)), hence $X \notin R_1$ (since $R_1 \subseteq R$). So $X \notin T_1$ and $X \notin R_1$ -- i.e., X is undecidable in (T_1).

Alternatively (and this proof is more constructive) let (T_1) be a formal sub-theory of (T). Then R_1^* is an r.e. set and is therefore representable in (T); let H represent it. Then the sentence H(h) is undecidable in (T) by Theorem 8, Chapter III.

§7. SOME SPECIAL THEORIES

In Tarski [32] a sequence of theories R, Q, P, N is considered, each being an extension of the preceeding. These theories play an important role in current research. The theory N is a saturated theory whose representable attributes are the arithmetic attributes. Hence all formal sub-theories of N are incomplete. P is a formal sub-theory of N -- it is the so called system of "Peano Arithmetic". Q is a formal sub-theory of P which contains only finitely many axioms -- this is the so-called "finitely axiomatizable" theory of Raphael Robinson. The system R is a formal sub-theory of Q which contains infinitely many axioms, but only five axiom <u>schemata</u>. The first three schemata immediately give the definability of plus and times. The last two immediately give the properties $C_1^!$, $C_2^!$, and hence conditions C_1, C_2 hold. Hence R -- as well as its consistent extensions Q and P -- is a Rosser theory.

§8. ESSENTIAL UNDECIDABILITY

Tarski calls a theory (T) <u>essentially undecidable</u> iff every consistent extension of (T) is undecidable. Consider now the representation system Z(T) associated with the theory (T). Every consistent extension (T') of (T) of course gives rise to an extension Z(T') of Z(T). However not every consistent extension of Z(T) is of the form Z(T') where T' is a theory. Now we know that all consistent extensions of Z(T) are undecidable iff the nuclei T_0, R_0 of (T) are recursively inseparable. Hence if (T_0, R_0) is R.I. then (T) is essentially undecidable. It remains an open problem whether the converse is true -- i.e., whether every essentially undecidable theory possesses recursively inseparable nuclei.

Tarski shows that a consistent theory in which all recursive functions are calculable is essentially undecidable. He also shows that all recursive functions are calculable in the system R. From this then follows the essential undecidability of R (as well, of course, as P and Q). In comparison, the methods of this study establish that R is a Rosser theory, and hence its nuclei T_o, R_o are recursively inseparable.

Sections §8, §9 [Presupposes Chapter V].

§9. ESSENTIAL CREATIVITY

Feferman [7] calls a theory (T) "essentially creative" iff every consistent formal extension of (T) is creative. We note that if (T_o, R_o) is effectively inseparable then (T) is certainly essentially creative. [This is an immediate consequence of the fact that if (γ_1, γ_2) is E.I., then every r.e. superset of γ_1 disjoint from γ_2 is creative -- this was shown in Chapter V.] So every consistent formal Rosser theory is essentially creative.

As a matter of fact, effective inseparability of the nuclei of a formal theory implies something still stronger than essential creativity: Let (T) be a consistent formal theory, let Σ be the collection of all r.e. supersets of T_o disjoint from R_o; let Σ_1 be the collection of all sets T_o', where (T') is a consistent formal extension of (T). It is clear that Σ_1 is a proper subset of Σ. The referee of Feferman's paper [6] suggested that (T) be called "effectively essentially creative" iff all elements of Σ_1 are uniformly creative (in the sense of §8 - Chapter V). Now we have shown (Chapter V - §11) that if (T_o, R_o) is E.I. then all elements of the larger collection Σ are uniformly creative, a-fortiori all elements of the smaller collection Σ_1 are then uniformly creative. Hence effective inseparability yields not only essential creativity, but even effective essential creativity in the above sense.

Feferman [7] shows that every consistent formal theory in which all recursive functions are definable and which satisfies conditions C_1', C_2' is essentially creative. Now the definability of all recursive functions in (T) obviously implies the enumerability in (T) of all r.e. sets. Hence by Theorem D we have the stronger theorem:

THEOREM F. Every theory (T) obeying Feferman's conditions is a Rosser theory and hence has E.I. nuclei (if consistent).

DISCUSSION. [For readers familiar with the definition of a theory (T) being interpretable or relatively interpretable in a theory (T'), cf. Tarski [32].]

Suppose (T) is interpretable or relative interpretable in (T'). Tarski has shown that if (T) is essentially undecidable, so is (T'). Feferman [7] subsequently extended this method to show that if (T) is essentially creative so is (T'). The author has shown [31] that if (T) has R.I. nuclei, so does (T'), and likewise with "E.I. nuclei".[1] Thus, Tarski's method of obtaining new essentially undecidable theories out of old, and Feferman's method of obtaining new essentially creative theories out of old can be extended to obtain new theories with R.I. (or E.I.) nuclei out of old.

§10. EXACT ROSSER THEORIES

In conclusion we discuss a recent result -- due jointly to Hilary Putnam and the author -- which extends an interesting result due jointly to Ehrenfeucht and Feferman [6].

Let us say that a predicate H exactly separates A from B within (T) iff H represents A and the negation H' of H represents B -- i.e., $A = H_T$ and $B = H_R$. [This condition is clearly a strengthening of the notion of "strong separability".] We shall call (T) an exact Rosser theory iff every disjoint pair of r.e. sets is exactly separable in (T).

We wish to show that if (T) is a Rosser theory in which all recursive functions of one argument are definable and if (T') is any formal extension of (T) which is simply consistent (without being necessarily ω-consistent) then not only are all r.e. sets representable in (T') (which is the result of Ehrenfeucht and Feferman) but that (T') is an exact Rosser theory.

We leave it to the reader to verify that if (A, B) is exactly separable in (T) and if f(x) is a function which is calculable in (T) then the pair $(f^{-1}(A), f^{-1}(B))$ is exactly separable in (T) -- exactly separated in fact by the formula $(Ex_2)\ [F(x_1, x_2) \wedge G(x_2)]$, where $F(x_1, x_2)$ is any formula which calculates the function f(x), and $G(x_1)$ is any formula which exactly separates (A, B) in (T). From this it follows that if all recursive functions of one argument are calculable in (T) and if at least one doubly universal pair of sets is exactly separable in (T) then (T) is an exact Rosser theory.

---

[1] We shall publish the details of this proof separately.

Suppose now that (T) is a formal consistent Rosser theory (or even a formal consistent theory in which at least one E.I. pair (γ_1, γ_2) of r.e. sets is strongly separated) and suppose that every recursive function of one argument is calculable in (T). Let H strongly separate (γ_1, γ_2) in (T). Then H_T, H_R are respective supersets of γ_1, γ_2 which are r.e. (since (T) is formal) and which are disjoint (since (T) is consistent). Then by Theorem 19, Chapter V, (H_T, H_R) is a doubly universal pair. And of course H exactly separates H_T from H_R in (T). Then by the preceeding paragraph (T) is an exact Rosser theory. Hence every consistent formal Rosser theory in which all recursive functions of one argument are calculable is an exact Rosser theory. Also if (T) is any Rosser theory in which all recursive functions of one argument are calculable then every consistent extension (T') of (T) is again a Rosser theory in which all recursive functions of one argument are calculable. Hence we have:

THEOREM G. [Putnam, Smullyan]. Let (T) be a Rosser theory in which all recursive functions of one argument are calculable. Then every consistent formal extension of (T) is an exact Rosser theory.

COROLLARY 1. Let (T) be a theory in which all recursive functions of one argument are calculable and which satisfies conditions C_1 and C_2. Then every consistent formal extension of (T) is an exact Rosser theory.

COROLLARY 2. The theories R, P, Q -- as well as all their simply consistent formal extensions -- are exact Rosser theories.

Sheperdson [23] has recently obtained an alternative proof of Corollary 2 which is extremely ingenious (it avoids appeal to the double universality of E.I. pairs of r.e. sets). In fact what properly results from Sheperdson's argument is that if (T) is a formal consistent Rosser theory for binary relations, then (T) is an exact Rosser theory for sets.

The argument is briefly as follows: Arrange all the binary predicates of (T) in some effective sequence $G_1, G_2, \ldots, G_n, \ldots$. Let α, β be disjoint sets of numbers (for the moment not necessarily r.e.). Let R_1 be the set of all ordered pairs (m, n) such that either $n \in \alpha$ or $G_n(m, n)$ is refutable; let R_2 be the set of all (m, n) such that either $m \in \beta$ or $G_n(m, n)$ is provable. Sheperdson shows that if $(R_1 - R_2)$ is strongly separable from $(R_2 - R_1)$ in (T) (where (T) is assumed consistent) then the set α is exactly separable from the set β in (T) -- in fact if G_p strongly separates $(R_1 - R_2)$ from $(R_2 - R_1)$ in (T) then the pair (α, β) is exactly separated in (T) by the formula $G_p(x_1, p)$. If now (T) is a formal theory and if α, β are both r.e. sets, then R_1, R_2 are both r.e. relations, so if (T) is also a Rosser theory for binary relations then $(R_1 - R_2)$ is strongly separable from $(R_2 - R_1)$ (cf. last paragraph §5.1) and so (α, β) is exactly separable in (T), which was to be proved.

REFERENCE AND BRIEF BIBLIOGRAPHY

[1] Bernays, Paul. Review of Myhill [14]. J. S. L. 22, 73-76.

[2] Church, Alonzo. Introduction to Mathematical Logic, Princeton University Press, Princeton, New Jersey, Vol. 1, 1956.

[3] Church, Alonzo. An Unsolvable Problem of Elementary Number Theory, American Journal of Mathematics, Vol. 58, 345-363.

[4] Church, Alonzo. The Calculi of Lambda-conversion, Annals of Mathematics Studies, No. 6, Princeton University Press, Princeton, New Jersey, 1941.

[5] Davis, Martin. Computability and Unsolvability, McGraw-Hill Series in Information Processing and Computers, 1958.

[6] Ehrenfeucht, A. and Feferman, S. "Representability of recursively enumerable sets in formal theories," Arch. Math. Logik Grundlagenforsch, Vol. 5 (1960), pp. 37-41.

[7] Feferman, S. Degrees of Unsolvability Associated with Classes of Formalized Theories, J. S. L. 22, 161-175.

[8] Gödel, Kurt. Uber formal unentscheidbare Sätze der Principia Mathematics und verwandter Systeme I, Montshefte für Mathematik and Physik, Vol. 38, 173-198, 1931.

[9] Gregorzyk, Andrzej. Some Classes of Recursive Functions. Rozprawy Matematyczne, Warszawa, 1953.

[10] Kalmár, Lázló. Eine einfache Konstruktion unentscheidbarer Sätze in formalen Systemen, Methodos, Vol. 2, 220-226, 1950.

[11] Kleene, Stephen C. Introduction to Metamathematics, D. Van Nostrand Company, Inc., Princeton, New Jersey, 1952.

[12] Muchnik, A. A. On the Separability of Recursively Enumerable Sets, Proceedings of the Academy of Science of the USSR, Vol. 109, No. 1.

[13] Muchnik, A. A. Isomorphisms of systems of recursively enumerable sets with effective properties. Tr. Mosk. Matem. O-va, Vol. 7 (1958), pp. 407-412.

[14] Myhill, John. Creative sets, Zeitschrift für mathematische Logik und Grundlagen der Mathematik, Vol. 1, 97-108, 1955.

[15] Myhill, John and Shepherdson, J. C. Effective Operations on Partial Recursive Functions, Zeitschrift für mathematische Logik und Grundlagen der Mathematik, Vol. 1, 310-317, 1955.

[16] Post, Emil L. Formal Reductions of the General Combinatorial Decision Problem, American Journal of Mathematics, Vol. 65, 197-215, 1943.

[17] Post, Emil L. Recursively Enumerable Sets of Positive Integers and Their Decision Problems, Bulletin of the American Mathematical Society, Vol. 50, 284-316, 1944.

[18] Putnam, H. Decidability and Essential Undecidability, J. S. L. 22, 39-54.

[19] Quine, W. V. Concatenation as a Basis for Arithmetic, J S. L. 11, 105-114.

[20] Quine, W. V. Mathematical Logic. Revised edition. Cambridge, Massachusetts, 346 pp.

[21] Robinson, Julia. Existential Definability in Arithmetic, Transactions of the American Mathematical Society, Vol. 72, 437-449, 1952.

[22] Rosser, Barkley. Extensions of Some Theorems of Gödel and Church, The Journal of Symbol Logic, Vol. 1, 87-91, 1936.

[23] Sheperdson, J. Representability of recursively enumerable sets in formal theories, to be published in Arch. Math. Logik Grundlagenforsch.

[24] Smullyan, R. M. Languages in Which Self-reference is Possible, J. S. L. 22, 55-67.

[25] Smullyan, R. M. Undecidability and Recursive Inseparability, Zeitschrift für mathematische Logik und Grundlagen der Mathematik, Vol. 4, 143-147.

[26] Smullyan, R. M. Elementary Formal Systems (Abstract). A. M. S. Bulletin 62, 600.

[27] Smullyan, R. M. Recursive Logics (Abstract). J. S. L. 21, 221.

[28] Smullyan, R. M. On Definability by Recursion (Abstract). A. M. S. Bulletin 62, 601.

[29] Smullyan, R. M. Creativity and Effective Inseparability (Abstract). J. S. L. 23, 458.

[30] Smullyan, R. M. Double Isomorphism of Rosser Theories (Abstract). A. M S. Notices 38, 277.

[31] Smullyan, R. M. Theory of Formal Systems. Doctoral dissertation, Princeton, May 1959. Also issued as Group Report 54-5, M. I. T. Lincoln Laboratory, April 15, 1959.

[32] Tarski, Alfred, Mostowski, Andrzej and Robinson, Raphael M. "Undecidable Theories," Studies in Logic and the Foundations of Mathematics, North-Holland Publishing Company, Amsterdam, 1953.

[33] Uspenskij, V. A. Gödels Theorem and the Theory of Algorithms (in Russian), Doklady Akademi nauk S.S.S.R., Vol 91, no. 4 (1953) 737-740.